ROY OF THE ROVERS

ROY OF THE ROVERS

THE PLAYING YEARS

Compiled by
PETER ACTON
and
COLIN M. JARMAN

Queen Anne Press

QUEEN ANNE PRESS
a division of Lennard Associates Limited
Mackerye End
Harpenden
Herts AL5 5DR

First published in Great Britain in 1994

British Library Cataloguing in Publication
is available

ISBN 1 85291 548 X

Cover illustration by Mike White
Design by Cooper Wilson
Origination by Capital Repro

Printed and bound in Slovenia

ACKNOWLEDGEMENTS
The authors would like to thank the following for their help, support and inspiration:-
Adrian Stephenson at Lennard Associates. Kim Jones, Molly and Les, Thomas David,
Peter and Patricia, Karen, Jeremy, Len and Rosalie. Jon Davidge, Michael Main, Chris
Power, Gil Page, Martin Morgan, Baz Spratley and all at Fleetway Editions. David Hunt,
Barrie Tomlinson, Stuart Green, Tom O'Callaghan, John Hall, Alan Vince, Gary Carter,
Leon Prynn, Gina Sussens, Claire Sawford and Paul Gravette. Charles Day, Melvin
Thomas, Ian Downs and all at CPL. Paul Cooper, Graham Curd, Steve Wilson, Maria
D'Orsi and Rob Shone at Cooper Wilson.

CONTENTS

50s

60s

70s

ROY RACE WAS THE GREATEST PLAYER IN THE HISTORY OF FOOTBALL. IN A CAREER SPANNING FIVE DECADES, HE REFLECTED THE CHANGING-FACE OF THE TOP-FLIGHT PLAYER – FROM MERCURIAL, BAGGY-SHORTED YOUTH OF THE 1950'S, TO THE POWERFULLY-BUILT GOAL-MACHINE OF THE 1990'S.

RACE THROUGH TIME

ROY RACE MAY HAVE CHANGED IN APPEARANCE THROUGHOUT HIS 40-YEAR CAREER, BUT WHAT REMAINED CONSTANT WAS THE FAMOUS RED AND YELLOW OF MELCHESTER ROVERS WHICH ROY ALWAYS WORE WITH PRIDE AND PASSION.

THE TOP SIX ROY ARTISTS FROM 1954...
JOE COLQUHOUN
PAUL TREVILLION
YVONNE HUTTON
DAVID SQUE
MIKE WHITE
BARRIE MITCHELL

80s

90s

INTRODUCTION

Everyone has heard of *Roy of the Rovers*, but few know the full history of this incredible comic strip saga which spanned 40 years.

For the first time ever, in 'The Playing Years' we have filled in those gaps of knowledge by providing a complete season-by-season illustrated history of *Roy of the Rovers* using the original comic strip.

The weekly *Roy of the Rovers* story started in the first issue of *Tiger* 'The Sport and Picture Story Weekly', which appeared on September 11th, 1954. The strip continued through 1976, with the launch of *Roy of the Rovers* comic, and ended with the closure of the comic on March 20th, 1993.

Tiger was the companion to *Lion,* a title which had been launched to compete with the hugely successful *Eagle* comic. Whilst *Eagle* starred pilot-of-the-future Dan Dare, *Tiger* chose a more down-to-earth sporting hero, who would not scale the heights instantly, but have to work hard for his victories. It took the young Roy Race, though exceptionally talented, a full year before he made the first team.

In documenting Roy's long-running career, our task has been condense over 6,500 pages of comic-strip into around 200 pages for this book.

Each season is summarised, pinpointing key developments – cup runs, signings, injuries, management bust-ups, league positions with reprints of what we believe to be the highlight games of that season. We have largely excluded the off-season holiday jaunts when Roy and the team would mark time before the next league campaign, embarking on lengthy overseas tours, mainly to South America, where they were usually kidnapped!

Because a single game could take many weeks to complete in the comic, we have occasionally resorted to edited highlights of a match, explaining the intervening action with additional or re-written captions within the comic strip. To ensure that our summaries were varied and readable, we introduced our own interpretive devices such as reports from the Melchester Gazette newspaper and Melchester radio match commentaries. The book concludes with a highlight section providing an at-a-glance summary of major events year-by-year.

Because an average of only three pages of *Roy* strip were published each week, the comic itself illustrated the season in broad brush strokes – one year concentrating on a cup run, the next on a league campaign. So, if *Roy of the Rovers:The Playing Years* neglects any aspects of a season, it is because they were not referred to in the comic. What we have succeeded in eliminating is the frustration felt by readers of the comic who had to wait until the next week's issue 'to find out what happens next'.

As we embarked on this project, we wondered whether Roy's story could be told in a biographical way as comic-book characters are often depicted in unconnected adventures with no regard to real time. But we were delighted to find that Roy's story could be reported as an unbroken historical progression. This was due to two key factors. Firstly the strip was created by a master comics-strip writer, the late Frank S. Pepper, who, we believe, based Melchester on the successful Arsenal side of the 1950s. Pepper created a strong cast of characters and an authentic team set-up. The *Roy* story was continued by a succession of writers of quality, the longest-serving being Tom Tully, who scripted the story for nearly 30 years.

Secondly, the *Roy* was harnessed to the framework of the football season, which always gave the strip a disciplined chronological structure. Hence we have been able to follow Roy's career at Rovers in the traditional football calendar starting with the 1954-55 season and ending with the tragically curtailed 1992-93 season.

We discovered a few references to the history of Melchester Rovers before 1954. We know that the club was founded in 1885 at Crib Lane, on the River Mel, one of the founders being Jonathan Drake. In 1905 Rovers were playing in the second division of the Southern League under the captaincy of Roy's grandfather, Billy Race, also a centre-forward. Under Billy, Rovers lifted the 1907 FA Cup. Although not detailed, there is also mention of Rovers being a successful side in the 1930s under manager George Armstrong. During this period the team won the League Championship three years in succession and 'reached the FA Cup final four times'. But it was not until the arrival of Roy Race and his pal Blackie Gray that Rovers found their 'glory years' and became the most successful club in the history of football.

Roy of the Rovers: The Playing Years is intended to provide a much needed tribute to Roy Race, whose story has touched the lives of millions of people over the years. It also serves as a testament to all those who worked on the comic for 40 years. If the book helps recapture the Melchester magic which graced the pages of this marvellous comic strip, then we have achieved our goal.

To quote the phrase that has become enshrined in the language of football commentators, we commend our readers to sit back and enjoy some
'Real Roy of The Rovers Stuff!'

Peter Acton
Colin M. Jarman

IN THE BEGINNING WAS THE WORD...
AND THE WORD WAS RACE!

Roy Race had recently started at his new school in Melchester, and his footballing ability soon gained him a place in the school's under-15 team. But in his first match, because of the scheming of his rival Bert Beston, Roy—with his pal Blackie Gray—arrived late and missed the kick-off. Melchester were disheartened and were losing 3-0. Roy managed to score one goal . . .

AT HALF-TIME THE CAPTAIN GAVE THE PLAYERS HIS PLAN FOR THE SECOND HALF...

ROY'S THE ONE WHO CAN SCORE—SO KEEP PUSHING THE BALL TO HIM ALL THE TIME.

...AND ROY KEEPS BANGING THE BALL PAST THEIR GOALKEEPER!

IT'S A TALL ORDER—BUT I'LL DO MY BEST.

THE MELCHESTER PLAYERS BEGAN GIVING THE BALL TO ROY AT EVERY OPPORTUNITY...

HARD LUCK, ROY, JUST WIDE!

MISTER LAMERTON, THE SPORTS-MASTER, LOOKED DOUBTFULLY AT ROY'S FATHER...

I THINK THE LADS HAVE MADE A MISTAKE...WHAT THEY'RE EXPECTING OF ROY IS TOO MUCH TO ASK OF ANY PLAYER!

ROY WON'T LET 'EM DOWN.

ROY GOT IN YET ANOTHER SHOT...

ROY'S DONE IT!

NOW WE'RE ONLY LOSING THREE-TWO!

THE OPPOSITION HAD SPOTTED WHAT WAS GOING ON...

WATCH THAT CHAP, DON'T LET HIM GET THE BALL.

BUT ROY PROVED AS ELUSIVE AS AN EEL...

ROY'S SCORED AGAIN!

WHAT A SHOT! HOW DID HE GET THAT ONE IN?

ROY'S SKIPPER WAS DELIGHTED...

GREAT STUFF, ROY! CAN YOU MANAGE ONE MORE?

I'LL DO MY BEST!

1951-55

9

MELCHESTER GRAMMAR SCHOOL

END OF TERM REPORT

Pupil: Roy Race

Class: 5A

Form Teacher: Mr M. O'Shaugnessy

MATHEMATICS – Roy has a good sense for all areas of mathematical study, most especially algebra and trigonometry, which he has shown an encouraging liking for.

ENGLISH LITERATURE – A careful reader, Roy has to be motivated to keep up with his studies, most especially with the English Classics and Shakespeare.

ENGLISH LANGUAGE – Has demonstrated the ability to eloquently transcribe his thoughts into poetry, and has shown an affinity for essay-writing.

SCIENCE - Roy's lack of interest in all matters scientific, except the annual field-trip, needs to be reversed.

PHYSICAL EDUCATION – A most athletic young man, Roy has shown an aptitude for all sports. In the past few months Roy has shown immense improvement in his football skills and would seem at his happiest with a ball at his feet. A most valuable member of the school football first eleven.

OVERALL – Roy must be persuaded not to let the sporting side of his nature exclude the more important aspects of his study. He has shown himself to be a very personable young fellow, well-liked by his class-mates and capable of taking discipline as well as showing leadership qualities. Well done Roy, keep up the good work.

TIGER

No. 1
WEEK ENDING
SEPTEMBER 11, 1954

3D

The SPORT and ADVENTURE PICTURE STORY WEEKLY

EVERY TUESDAY

PLEASE TURN TO BACK PAGE

ROY WAS ASTOUNDED WHEN HE REALISED WHO ALF LEEDS WAS

YOU MEAN YOU'RE GIVING ME A CHANCE TO PLAY FOR THE ROVERS?

THAT'S RIGHT, LAD. YOU MIGHT FIT INTO OUR "A" TEAM. IF YOU'RE INTERESTED, COME AND SEE ME AT THE STADIUM AT 11 O'CLOCK ON MONDAY

ROY WAS THRILLED TO THE CORE. HE HAD OFTEN DREAMED OF PLAYING FOR A CLUB LIKE MELCHESTER ROVERS, BUT NEVER REALISED HE WAS GOOD ENOUGH EVEN TO BE CONSIDERED. IT WAS A CHANCE TOO GOOD TO MISS. MONDAY MORNING FOUND HIM OUTSIDE THE ROVERS' FAMOUS STADIUM

ROY GASPED AS HE GAZED AT THE IMPOSING ENTRANCE OF THE STADIUM

GOSH, WHAT A DIFFERENCE FROM OUR OLD HUT!

ROY WALKED BOLDLY IN THROUGH THE SWING DOORS, AND THEN ---

HEY, WHERE DO YOU THINK YOU'RE GOING?

MR. LEEDS TOLD ME TO COME AND SEE HIM

JUNIORS AREN'T ALLOWED TO USE THIS ENTRANCE, LAD. COME WITH ME -- I'LL PUT YOU RIGHT

SO YOU'RE ANOTHER OF 'EM WHO WANTS TO BE A ROVER? A LOT TRY, BUT NOT MANY LAST THE PACE. IF YOU CAN STICK IT, IT'S A GRAND LIFE

IF THEY'LL HAVE ME, I'LL STICK IT O.K. ---

THE FRIENDLY DOORMAN POINTED OUT THE WAY

THERE'S THE ENTRANCE TO THE JUNIOR GROUND. THAT'S THE ONE YOU'LL USE IN FUTURE. GOOD LUCK!

THANKS A LOT -- I'LL REMEMBER

THE SIGHT OF THE ROVERS' TRAINING QUARTERS TOOK ROY'S BREATH AWAY

WEST ENCLOSURE

GOSH, WHAT A CLUB TO BELONG TO! I HOPE MR. LEEDS WON'T CHANGE HIS MIND

AUGUST '54

Alf Leeds did not change his mind – he knew when a young lad had the right stuff in his boots. He could see that Roy would be a future star.

SEPTEMBER '54

Young Roy Race soon made a name for himself in the youth team, alongside his schoolboy chum Blackie Gray.
   The two lads quickly built up a telepathic understanding, on and off the pitch. Both team-mates improved their play until...

DECEMBER '54

...It wasn't long before Roy and Blackie were playing in the Rovers' "A" team and Roy quickly notched his first "senior" goal...

...FROM A PERFECTLY WEIGHTED PASS FROM BLACKIE.

THESE TWO LADS ARE WORKING WONDERS...IT WON'T BE LONG BEFORE THEY ARE BOTH IN ROVERS' FIRST TEAM!

PROMOTION TO A LEAGUE OF BOYS' OWN

AUG '55 – ROY RACE AND BLACKIE GRAY MADE THEIR FIRST TEAM DEBUTS v ELBURY WANDERERS

THE RIVAL FANS EAGERLY DISCUSSED THE CHANCES OF THEIR TEAMS.

GOOD LUCK, ROVERS! YOUR LADS'LL NEED IT TO STOP OUR INSIDE-RIGHT! HEDLOW'S THE HOTTEST SHOT IN FOOTER-BOOTS!

WE'LL SEE ABOUT THAT MATE! WE'VE GOT TWO NEW FORWARDS IN OUR LINE-UP!

THAT'S RIGHT-- ROY RACE AND BLACKIE GRAY

GET YOUR FAVOURS

INSIDE THE GROUND...

WHAT ARE OUR TWO NEW FORWARDS LIKE?

I SAW 'EM PLAY WITH THE RESERVES LAST SEASON, AND BELIEVE ME, ROY AND BLACKIE MAKE A FINE PARTNERSHIP!

THAT WAS WITH THE RESERVES! PLAYING WITH THE FIRST TEAM WON'T BE SO EASY

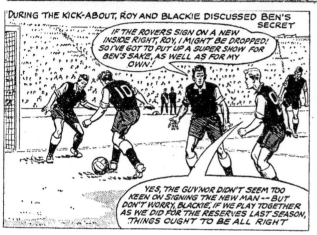

DURING THE KICK-ABOUT, ROY AND BLACKIE DISCUSSED BEN'S SECRET

IF THE ROVERS SIGN ON A NEW INSIDE RIGHT, ROY, I MIGHT BE DROPPED! SO I'VE GOT TO PUT UP A SUPER SHOW FOR BEN'S SAKE, AS WELL AS FOR MY OWN!

YES, THE GUV'NOR DIDN'T SEEM TOO KEEN ON SIGNING THE NEW MAN -- BUT DON'T WORRY, BLACKIE, IF WE PLAY TOGETHER AS WE DID FOR THE RESERVES LAST SEASON, THINGS OUGHT TO BE ALL RIGHT

THE PALS STRUCK THEIR BEST FORM RIGHT FROM THE KICK-OFF, THEN THE CROWD ROARED AS BLACKIE SNAPPED UP THE BALL, AND SENT A PERFECT THROUGH PASS TO ROY

BLACKIE'S CERTAINLY ON TOP FORM! NOW IT'S UP TO ME!

ROY FLICKED THE BALL PAST AN ELBURY BACK, FOLLOWED UP AND SHOT FIRST TIME

GOAL!

GOOD OLD ROY! UP THE ROVERS!

BY THUNDER! THAT NEW LAD RACE CAN CERTAINLY SHOOT!

AS THE FIRST HALF PROGRESSED, THE PALS DOMINATED THE ROVERS' ATTACKS. THEIR LIGHTNING SHORT-PASSES KEPT THE FANS ROARING WITH DELIGHT, AND THE ELBURY GOALIE HAD TO BE ON HIS TOES. THEN A BRILLIANT HEADER FROM THE ROVERS' INSIDE-LEFT PUT THEM TWO-UP!

ROVERS CONTINUED TO PRESS. SUDDENLY, DISASTER STRUCK!

GOSH, CHARLIE'S STOPPED A NASTY ONE!

!

AGH!

CHARLIE KING, THE ROVERS' RIGHT-WINGER, COLLAPSED GROANING. IN A FLASH, TRAINER TAFF MORGAN RACED ON TO THE FIELD

I-I'M SORRY, MELCHESTER, IT WAS A COMPLETE ACCIDENT!

FAIR ENOUGH! COULDN'T BE HELPED! HOW IS HE, TAFF?

NOT TOO GOOD, SKIPPER. HE'S PULLED A LEG MUSCLE BADLY! HE'LL HAVE TO GO OFF!

AS CHARLIE WAS CARRIED OFF, SKIPPER ANDY McDONALD TURNED ANXIOUSLY TO ROY AND BLACKIE

IT LOOKS AS IF POOR OLD CHARLIE'S HAD IT FOR THIS GAME, BLACKIE. YOU'D BETTER MOVE OUT TO THE WING IN HIS PLACE. WE'LL HAVE TO PLAY FOUR FORWARDS

WHAT ROTTEN LUCK FOR CHARLIE!

IT'S BAD LUCK FOR YOU TOO, BLACKIE! PLAYING ON THE WING NOT ONLY SPOILS OUR SHORT-PASSING GAME, BUT IT LESSENS YOUR CHANCE OF SHOWING THAT THE ROVERS NEEDN'T BUY A NEW INSIDE-RIGHT!

FACING TEN MEN, ELBURY PULLED BACK A GOAL THANKS TO A HEADER BY ENGLAND FORWARD ARTY HEDLOW. WITH BLACKIE GRAY FORCED TO PLAY OUTSIDE RIGHT, ROVERS WORKED TIRELESSLY FOR A DECISIVE THIRD GOAL.

1955-56

13

BUT BLACKIE, WITH NO INSIDE-RIGHT, COULD NOT WORK HIS SHORT PASSING GAME WITH ROY, AND THE ELBURY DEFENDERS HAD HIS CENTRES WELL COVERED

BLACKIE'S DOING HIS BEST, BUT HE'S TRYING TO DO THE WORK OF TWO MEN!

FROM ONE NEAT CLEARANCE, THE BALL WENT STRAIGHT TO ARTY HEDLOW, THE WANDERERS' FAMOUS INSIDE-RIGHT

HEDLOW WENT RIGHT THROUGH ON HIS OWN, THE BALL SEEMINGLY GLUED TO HIS TOES, THEN —

GOAL! GOAL!

GOOD OLD ARTY! WHAT AN EQUALISER!

HEDLOW RUSHED BACK TO HIS TEAM-MATES, HAND OUTSTRETCHED, DELIBERATELY SEEKING THEIR CONGRATULATIONS. ROY AND BLACKIE WATCHED CRITICALLY

WELL, HEDLOW CERTAINLY WANTS EVERYONE TO KNOW HE SCORED THAT GOAL!

HE'S A DARNED GOOD INSIDE-RIGHT, ROY, BUT DOESN'T HE KNOW IT! LOOK HOW HE'S SHOWING OFF!

ROVERS 2 ELBURY 2

THE YOUNG PALS SOON STRUGGLED TO KEEP UP WITH THE PACE....

BLACKIE REALISED THAT HE HAD TO ACT QUICKLY, AND BEFORE THE DEFENDER COULD TACKLE, HE SENT OVER A CURLING CENTRE. ROY LEAPT HIGH, BUT THE ELBURY CENTRE HALF JUST ROBBED HIM OF THE BALL

WE'RE FAIRLY MESSING UP OUR CHANCES TO SHOW WHAT WE CAN DO! WE CAN'T SEEM TO GET GOING AT ALL NOW. AT THIS RATE, BLACKIE AND I WILL BE BACK IN THE RESERVES FOR GOOD!

PLAY MOVED TO THE ROVERS' LEFT WING, BUT AN ELBURY HALF-BACK BROKE UP THE ATTACK, AND CLEARED TO HEDLOW, WHO WAS MOVING TOWARDS GOAL

THE BALL DROPPED AWKWARDLY, BUT QUICK AS A FLASH, HEDLOW CUNNINGLY FLICKED IT UNDER CONTROL WITH HIS HAND

HEY! HANDS, REF!

BUT NO WHISTLE SHRILLED, FOR THE REFEREE HAD BEEN UNSIGHTED, AND HEDLOW SLAMMED THE BALL INTO THE NET

GOAL!

NO GOAL! WHAT ABOUT THE HANDS, REF?

REFEREE MR BLACK ALLOWED THE GOAL AND ELBURY WERE IN FRONT...

FIVE MINUTES LATER, BLACKIE SUDDENLY RACED INTO THE CENTRE OF THE FIELD, AND WHIPPED THE BALL OFF AN ELBURY MAN'S TOE

THAT'S MORE LIKE IT! I HOPE ROY'S IN POSITION

ROY DASHED THROUGH TO PICK UP BLACKIE'S SKILFUL PASS

GOOD OLD BLACKIE! NOW'S MY CHANCE TO EQUALISE!

AS AN ELBURY BACK LEAPT TO TACKLE, ROY SLAMMED THE BALL GOALWARDS

GOAL! THREE~ALL!

WELL DONE, ROY! LET'S HAVE ANOTHER!

BUT THE FINAL WHISTLE BLEW WITH NO FURTHER SCORE. THEN AS THE TEAMS TROTTED OFF, ARTY HEDLOW OVERTOOK ROY

NOT A BAD SHOW, KID! BUT YOU'RE NOT QUITE UP TO THIS CLASS OF SOCCER YET. I GUESS YOU AND GRAY WILL BE BACK IN THE RESERVES NEXT WEEK. TOUGH LUCK!

FINAL SCORE – ROVERS 3   ELBURY 3

AUGUST '55

ROVERS SIGN HEDLOW

Melchester Rovers broke the bank to sign Elbury Wanderers' Arty Hedlow for a record £10,000. Hedlow will replace Blackie Gray at Cobdale United on Saturday, alongside Roy Race, who like Gray made his senior League debut against Elbury. Roy, grandson of former Rovers' captain Billy Race – scored twice and looks set to follow in his legendary grandfather's boots. Manager Ben Galloway said of his new striking partnership, "Playing alongside an international player of Hedlow's calibre, young Roy will blossom into a player with a great future ahead of him. I expect Roy to listen and learn a lot from his new mentor....."

DURING THE HALF-TIME INTERVAL –

WE OUGHT TO BE LEADING INSTEAD OF BEING ONE DOWN! YOU REFUSED TO LISTEN TO MY ADVICE, ROY. YOU HOGGED THE BALL, AND THEN FUNKED IT WHENEVER YOU CAME UP AGAINST THAT HEAVYWEIGHT COBDALE CENTRE-HALF!

ROY LEAPT ANGRILY TO HIS FEET

I'M NOT TAKING THAT FROM YOU, HEDLOW! YOU'VE BEEN MOANING AT ME ALL THE FIRST HALF, AND MAKING SURE THE OTHERS DIDN'T HEAR. BUT NOBODY CALLS ME A FUNK! I'D LIKE TO KNOCK YOUR THUNDERING BLOCK OFF!

OVERHEARING ROY'S ANGRY WORDS, SKIPPER ANDY McDONALD RUSHED FORWARD

CUT THAT OUT, ROY! HAVE YOU GONE COMPLETELY CRAZY?

THE MISERABLE YOUNG SWEEP LOST HIS TEMPER, JUST BECAUSE I TRIED TO GIVE HIM A BIT OF GOOD ADVICE

JUST THEN, THE WARNING BELL SOUNDED FOR THE TEAMS TO RETURN. AS THEY CAME OUT, ARTY COULDN'T RESIST A FURTHER JIBE AT ROY

YOU'RE ASKING TO BE PUT BACK INTO THE RESERVES WITH YOUR PAL BLACKIE GRAY--AND I SHAN'T BE BROKEN-HEARTED IF THAT HAPPENS!

O.K.! YOU'VE GOT THE BEST OF IT NOW, HEDLOW, BUT SOONER OR LATER, THE OTHERS'LL FIND OUT JUST WHAT A ROTTER YOU ARE!

ROY CONTINUED TO FUNK AGAINST BIG RON BLAKE....

ROY CRASHED TO THE GROUND, BADLY SHAKEN, BUT HE WASN'T BEATEN, YET

EVEN AS BLAKE WAS ABOUT TO CLEAR THE BALL, ROY JUST MANAGED TO PUSH IT TO HEDLOW WITH A DESPERATE LUNGE

THE CROWD ROARED AS HEDLOW SNAPPED UP THE BALL, SWERVED, RAN ON, AND SLAMMED IT INTO THE NET

ROVERS 1   COBDALE 1

YOUNG ROY HAD WORKED HARD TO EARN HIS PLACE IN ROVERS' FIRST TEAM...

1   LEN DOLLAND
2   DAVE WILLIAMS
3   DOUG ROBERTS
4   HUGH GRIFFITHS
5   ANDY MCDONALD
6   BUSTER BROWN
7   CHARLIE KING
8   ARTY HEDLOW
9   ROY RACE
10 JIM HALLETT
11 TOM DAWSON

...BUT FOR HOW LONG?

ROY GOT THE BETTER OF BLAKE IN A TOUCHLINE TUSSLE....

WHILE BLAKE WAS STILL SPRAWLING, ROY SCRAMBLED TO HIS FEET AND GRABBED THE BALL

WITH A SUPERB THROW, ROY SENT THE BALL STRAIGHT TO ARTY HEDLOW

THE LIGHTNING MOVE CAUGHT COBDALE COMPLETELY OFF-GUARD, AND HEDLOW CRASHED THE BALL, FIRST-TIME, INTO THE NET

FINAL SCORE – ROVERS 2   COBDALE 1

HEDLOW KNEE BLOW

Rovers' goal ace Arty Hedlow has been struck down by a mystery knee injury. No official reason has been given for the sudden complaint, but it will keep Rovers' top scorer out of action for a few weeks. Hedlow, with 24 goals in 26 games, has helped steer Rovers to their highest league position for six years. A very frustrated manager Ben Galloway commented, "Just as our season was taking off, we are struck down by ill-fortune. Hedlow has been in his best form for many years

and the £10,000 he cost us was money well spent."

Hedlow has struck up a great understanding with teenage sensation Roy Race, whose 9 goals have surpassed Galloway's wildest dreams, "I knew it needed a special player to coax out the true talent Roy revealed in Rovers' reserves and Hedlow has done just that. Now we shall see how Roy copes without his senior partner."

Blackie Gray seems certain to replace

Hedlow at inside-right and continue the understanding with Race that developed in the "A" team last season. Gray has played only one game for the senior team this campaign and will be keen to make the most of his opportunity.

If Hedlow's injury is long-term, even an outstanding performance from Gray may not be enough to stop Rovers' chairman Mr Mason again looking outside the club for a more experienced forward.

FEBRUARY '56

Six months after making his senior debut, Blackie Gray returned to first team action, and put on a solo show that defied the snow and title-chasing Hamville.

Taking daredevil risks on the icy pitch, Gray cancelled out the visitor's early lead, with a spectacular bicycle kick that would have caused cardiac arrest in the heat of the Maracana Stadium.

With a freak injury, rumoured to have involved club mascot Billy the goat, sidelining

Arty Hedlow, Blackie seized his chance with both feet and grew in confidence. As others floundered around him, he picked his way around Melchester Stadium. Seconds after making a daredevil goal-line clearance, the teenage inside-forward raced the length of the pitch to be first to a loose ball in the Hamville penalty area and found the net with a low skidding icy blast.

With this victory Rovers strengthened their title ambitions, but despite Gray's heroics, manager Ben Galloway knew Rovers' season hinged on Hedlow's knee injury.

In a Radio Melchester interview, the manager spoke of mixed fortunes for the club, "I am very pleased for Blackie. He was unlucky to be dropped to make way for Hedlow, at the start of the season and he showed us what a talented teenager he is. From now until the end of the season, the team will have a tough battle and will need all the experience we can get. It will be a baptism of fire for youngsters like Roy Race and Gray. I am confident they will make a fist of it."

	P	W	D	L	F	A	Pts
Portdean City	28	18	6	4	64	23	42
Hamville	26	16	7	3	57	26	39
Welbeck Wdrs	27	16	5	6	60	28	37
Langton Utd	28	14	8	6	51	27	36
Melchester R	27	15	5	7	49	29	35

MARCH '56

HEDLOW OUT FOR SEASON

Following surgery on Arty Hedlow's injured knee, doctors have ruled him out for at least two months. Ben Galloway is now left with a difficult decision – either to buy another proven forward or stick with the youthful attacking partnership of Race and Gray that destroyed Hamville last Saturday.

MARCH '56

F.A. CUP HORROR!

Melchester Rovers 1 Storford United 2

In the sixth round of the F.A. Cup, high-flying Rovers had their wings clipped by lowly Storford in a tense battle that saw Rovers squander a handful of goal chances. Teenage strikers Roy Race and Blackie Gray (despite five goals in his last three games) failed to hit the target and Rovers' late consolation goal came from captain Andy McDonald. Without the distraction of the Cup, Rovers can now focus all their attention on reversing their dismal run of form in the League.

APRIL '56

ROVERS LOSING STREAK

Charnley Athletic 3 Melchester Rovers 0

... As Rovers' slump continues, worse news reached Galloway when it was announced that Hedlow's knee injury has not improved and he will not play football again. This has shattered Rovers' season and Galloway must again rebuild his team.

MAY '56 PROGRAMME NOTES V BAMFORD

In the past few seasons, when Rovers reached the last game of the season, we have often looked back on a season full of problems off the field of play, and little to celebrate on it. This has been a season that had promised much but leaves us wanting more. It has proved that the fire in Melchester Rovers has not been fully extinguished - it burns yet with a faint ember. Our squad of young players can breathe life back into the glowing coals and rekindle the past glories of this once great football club. It may take a few years to bring the club and its burgeoning talent to the top - but the name of Melchester Rovers will be back where it belongs - on the great football trophies of the land.

Finally, I wish Arty Hedlow all the best for his future as the new manager of Dunbar City in the Southern League. He may have only been a Rovers' player for half a season but he left a great impression on us all.

BEN GALLOWAY

THE LOSS OF HEDLOW, MEANT ROY WOULD BEAR THE BRUNT OF ROVERS' GOAL-SCORING DUTIES.

FINAL SCORE – ROVERS 1 BAMFORD 0

JUNE '56

ROVERS "YOUNG PLAYER OF THE YEAR" – ROY RACE

The one constant light that shone brightly through Rovers' roller-coaster season belonged to teenage centre-forward Roy Race. His twelve goals in his first senior sea-

son surely points the way to many more to come. When asked about his first full season in the senior team, young Roy replied, "I am glad both Blackie Gray and I scored a number of goals each. We played together at school, youth and "A" level, and now in the senior team. It is a wonderful feeling, I just hope we can go on playing together forever. I'd give my left foot not to have to ever hang my boots up."

ON A WING AND A PIERRE

AUGUST '56

ROVERS IMPORT FRENCH WINGER

Ben Galloway, Melchester Rovers' manager, has returned from his team's pre-season trip to France with something to declare – a new player! Galloway has picked up crack right winger Pierre Dupont from French side Rochemont, to play alongside Rovers' gifted young striking duo, Roy Race and Blackie Gray.

Despite playing on the losing side – Rovers triumphed over Rochemont 3-2 –

Dupont so impressed Mr Galloway that he started negotiations with the French management immediately and struck a deal to bring the dashing Dupont to Melchester Stadium for a short term trial.

Rovers are playing down his arrival, in spite of the inevitable local excitement surrounding a new continental star. "This is simply an experiment and we don't want to disrupt the other members of the team by

making a fuss over his arrival," Mr Galloway told us. Neither would he be drawn on the financial details of the signing.

Nevertheless, low-key or not, Dupont's presence will certainly put 'le chat amongst the pidgins' at Melchester Stadium. The Frenchman's arrival is certain to jeopardise the ambitions of Rovers' right wing specialist, Sam Higby, who must feel threatened by Monsieur Dupont.

AUG '56

In his first game for Rovers, against Welbeck Wanderers, Pierre Dupont soon made his mark with a spectacular shot to open his goal account.

SEP '56

Rovers, strengthened by the imaginative Pierre Dupont, were about to take the field in a league match at table-topping Portdean City. But jealous winger Sam Higby, who had been dropped in favour of the Frenchman, had ensured that Dupont would miss the start of the game.

SECONDS BEFORE THE OFF, DUPONT WAS STILL MISSING AND HIGBY WAS READY TO TAKE HIS PLACE...

PIERRE HAD SOME EXPLAINING TO DO...

PIERRE RUSHED STRAIGHT TO BEN GALLOWAY

MY SORROWS, M'SIEUR GALLOWAY! I TRIED MY UTMOST TO GET 'ERE SOONER, BUT IT IS NOT MY FAULT ZAT I AM LATE! I WAS LOCKED UP DELIBERATELY BY—BY SOMEONE! CAN I PLAY, M'SIEUR?

CALM DOWN, DUPONT! NOW, WHAT IN THUNDER ARE YOU TALKING ABOUT?

PIERRE POURED OUT THE FULL STORY OF HIS STRANGE ADVENTURE IN THE LIGHTHOUSE. AT THE FINISH, BEN FROWNED DOUBTFULLY, THEN~

IT'S A FANTASTIC STORY, DUPONT, BUT THERE'S NO TIME TO CHECK ON IT NOW. ALL RIGHT—GET CHANGED QUICKLY! YOU'LL PLAY EVEN IF THE MATCH STARTS WITHOUT YOU

WITH A WHOOP OF DELIGHT, PIERRE RUSHED TO GET HIS PLAYING TOGS. BUT HIGBY WAS FURIOUS

YOU CAN'T DO THIS, GUV'NOR! WHY SHOULD I STAND DOWN FOR DUPONT AT THE LAST MINUTE? YOU TOLD ME I COULD PLAY!

I GIVE THE ORDERS, HIGBY — NOT YOU! NOW SHUT UP AND TRY AND ACT LIKE A SPORTSMAN!

WITHOUT ANOTHER WORD OF PROTEST, HIGBY SLUNK AWAY, TO CHANGE BACK INTO HIS ORDINARY TOGS

HOW IN THUNDER DID THAT DARNED FRENCHMAN ESCAPE? WELL, IF HE THINKS I'M TAKING THIS LYING DOWN HE'S MISTAKEN! I'LL STOP AT NOTHING NOW TO GET THE ROTTER SLUNG OUT OF THE ROVERS!

WHILE PIERRE WAS CHANGING, THE REST OF THE TEAM RAN OUT INTO THE FULL FURY OF THE WIND

HERE THEY COME!

UP THE ROVERS

WOW! WHAT A GALE! HERE'S HOPING WE WIN THE TOSS!

BUT WHEN THE REF. CALLED THE CAPTAINS TOGETHER--

HEADS!

IT'S TAILS!

GOOD FOR US! YOU BET WE'LL KICK WITH THE WIND!

BEFORE THE ROVERS KICKED OFF, THE PORTDEAN SKIPPER HAD A QUICK WORD WITH HIS FORWARDS

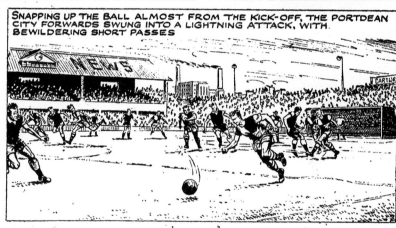

DON'T GET OVER-CONFIDENT BECAUSE THE WIND'S IN OUR FAVOUR. KEEP THE BALL DOWN, AND KEEP IT MOVING. SHORT SHARP PASSES ~ AND LET'S GO ALL OUT FOR THREE QUICK GOALS BEFORE THE ROVERS SETTLE DOWN

SNAPPING UP THE BALL ALMOST FROM THE KICK-OFF, THE PORTDEAN CITY FORWARDS SWUNG INTO A LIGHTNING ATTACK, WITH BEWILDERING SHORT PASSES

THE ROVERS' DEFENDERS, HAMPERED BY THE WIND BEATING INTO THEIR FACES, WERE BEATEN BY THE SPEED OF THAT BRILLIANT OPENING PORTDEAN ATTACK.

THE CITY'S CENTRE-FORWARD RACED INTO THE GOAL-AREA, WHIPPED UP A LIGHTNING PASS FROM HIS LEFT-WINGER, AND CRASHED THE BALL INTO THE NET

GOAL!

GOAL! UP THE CITY!

GOSH! A GOAL DOWN IN THE FIRST MINUTE! WE'LL HAVE TO PULL OUR SOCKS UP!

1956-57

BY THE TIME PIERRE FOUND HIS FEET, ROVERS WERE THREE GOALS DOWN. BUT THE FRENCHMAN WAS SOON LINKING UP WITH ROY RACE...

PIERRE DODGED A PLUNGING BACK, AND THEN, AS ANOTHER CITY MAN SHAPED TO TACKLE, HE FLICKED THE BALL TO ROY.

BUT AT THAT MOMENT, A SHEET OF NEWSPAPER, BLOWN ACROSS THE PITCH BY THE GALE, FLAPPED RIGHT INTO ROY'S FACE. HE MISKICKED, AND THE BALL WENT WIDE OF THE GOAL.

BEFORE ROY COULD RECOVER, THE REF'S WHISTLE SHRILLED FOR HALF-TIME --

ROY SOON POUNCED IN THE SECOND HALF...

ACTING WITH INCREDIBLE SPEED, ROY HOOKED THE BALL SIDEWAYS -- AND THE TWO BACKS CRASHED INTO EACH OTHER!

NEXT MOMENT, ROY STEADIED THE BALL AND THEN SHOT. THE CITY GOALIE MADE A DESPAIRING DIVE, BUT--

ROY'S GOAL GAVE THE ROVERS NEW HEART, AND THEY WERE DETERMINED TO WIN, ALTHOUGH IT MEANT SCORING THREE MORE GOALS.
A FEW MINUTES LATER THEY SWEPT INTO THE CITY GOAL-AREA, AND INSIDE-RIGHT BLACKIE GRAY CRASHED IN THE SECOND GOAL.

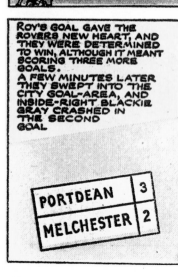

| PORTDEAN | 3 |
| MELCHESTER | 2 |

PORTDEAN WERE NOW ON THE DEFENSIVE, BUT TIME WAS RUNNING SHORT FOR THE ROVERS. THEN, WITH ONLY A FEW MINUTES LEFT, PIERRE DUPONT, THE ROVERS' FRENCH RIGHT-WINGER, GATHERED A PASS AND STREAKED DOWN THE WING.

THE LITTLE BUNCH OF ROVERS' FANS CHEERED WILDLY AS PIERRE DODGED A CITY HALF, AND RACED THROUGH TO THE GOAL AREA.

PIERRE SHAPED FOR A SHOT AT GOAL...

20

THE CITY LEFT-BACK TACKLED DESPERATELY, BUT PIERRE CRASHED IN A TERRIFIC SHOT. IT LOOKED A WINNER ALL THE WAY, BUT THE GOALIE MANAGED TO GRAB IT

ROY HAD FOLLOWED UP, AND BEFORE THE GOALIE COULD RECOVER HIS BALANCE, HE WAS CHARGED OVER THE LINE, STILL HOLDING THE BALL

GOAL! GOOD OLD ROY!

IT WAS THE EQUALIZER AND EVEN THE DISMAYED CITY SUPPORTERS JOINED IN THE CHEERS. BUT THOUGH PORTDEAN'S CONFIDENCE WAS BADLY SHAKEN, THEY MADE ONE LAST DETERMINED... ATTEMPT TO REGAIN THE LEAD. THEY FLUNG EVERYTHING INTO ATTACK, BUT PLUCKY LEN DOLLAND, ROVERS' GOALIE, KEPT THE BALL OUT WITH SOME MIRACULOUS SAVES. THEN, WITH THE SCORES STILL LEVEL, AND FULL-TIME ALMOST DUE, THE ROVERS AGAIN SURGED INTO THE CITY GOAL AREA.

BLACKIE GRAY LEAPT FOR A HIGH CENTRE, AND NODDED IT GOAL'WARDS, BUT THE BALL HIT THE BAR!

AS THE BALL REBOUNDED, INSIDE LEFT JIM HALLETT CRASHED IT BACK INTO GOAL, BUT THE GOALIE JUST GOT TO IT!

THE CITY MEN PACKED THEIR GOALMOUTH, THEN, WITH BARE SECONDS LEFT, PIERRE SHOT HARD AND LOW FOR THE CORNER OF THE NET — ONLY FOR A SPRAWLING DEFENDER TO GET HIS BOOT TO IT!

THE BALL BOUNCED CLEAR OF THE GOAL. PLAYERS SCRAMBLED FRANTICALLY TO GET TO IT — THEN ROY LEAPT INTO THE AIR, CAUGHT THE BALL ON THE VOLLEY, AND CRASHED IT INTO THE NET

FULL TIME CAME BEFORE THE GAME COULD RESTART, AND THE VICTORIOUS ROVERS TROTTED DELIGHTEDLY OFF THE FIELD

WELL DONE, ROY! I NEVER THOUGHT WE'D DO IT! IT WAS THE TOUGHEST GAME WE'VE PLAYED THIS SEASON!

YOU'RE TELLING ME, BLACKIE! BUT WE'D NEVER HAVE WON IF PIERRE HADN'T BEEN PLAYING!

MA FOI! YOU PRAISE ME TOO 'IGH, ROY! YOU WON ZE GAME — NOT ME!

PIERRE'S GALLIC CHARM INSPIRED ROVERS ONTO NEW HEIGHTS OF ACHIEVEMENT...AND THE TEAM LOOKED FORWARD TO A SUCCESSFUL CUP RUN...

JAN '57 – FA Cup 3rd Round
Carnbrook Town 1   Rovers 2
Race, Dupont

FEB '57 – FA Cup 4th Round
Rovers 1   Bronton City 2
Race

MAY '57 – Rovers v Salthampton
In their last game of the season, thanks to a solitary Roy Race goal, Rovers defeated Salthampton to finish fourth in the first division...their highest post-war position. Rovers would aim higher next season.

DIVISION ONE LEAGUE TABLE – TOP FIVE

	P	W	D	L	F	A	P
Langton United	42	25	13	4	110	40	63
Elbury Wanderers	42	22	14	6	101	43	58
Portdean City	42	21	15	6	93	53	57
Melchester Rovers	42	17	18	7	111	60	52
Welbeck Wanderers	42	18	16	8	106	58	52

1956-57

'BIG MAC' RELISHES HIS LAST SEASON

"I'LL GIVE IT ONE LAST SHOT" VOWS ROVERS' VETERAN SKIPPER

Andy McDonald, Melchester Rovers' veteran centre-half and skipper, has ended months of speculation by announcing that he is not yet ready to hang up his boots.

Rumours that he has played his last game for the club have been swept away. Andy told us he is determined to give his all for one more season in a final bid to achieve his goal of steering Rovers to their first post-war league title.

"I've had twelve years at Rovers, but so far without any cup or championship honours. Before I go, I'm determined to set Rovers back on the road to the success they enjoyed in the glory days before the war."

But has "Big Mac" left it too late, can the old sea-dog's legs stand up to the punishment of one more gruelling season? It would be sad to see the lad from Glasgow bow out a shadow of his former self.

MELCHESTER ROVERS – THE STUFF CHAMPIONS ARE MADE OF

Melchester Rovers 3   Salthampton 2

Having rekindled their game-winning form Rovers were now lying in tenth place in the league. They now faced their most difficult challenge of the season so far, against the mighty table-topping Salthampton whose goal-scoring power had been the sensation of the season.

Salthampton set out their stall before a capacity Melchester Stadium crowd, emboldened by an unbeaten record largely down to their famous goal-scoring partnership of 'Buck' Taylor and Jeff Tomlins. The duo's unique "Double Centre-Forward Move" had cut swathes through opposition defences all season.

Two-nil down at half-time, Rovers looked out of the hunt. But, displaying a footballing brain beyond his modest years, young Roy Race spiked the 'Salts' twin-spearheaded attack with a cleverly executed tactic. He fell back to form a "Double Centre-Half" duo with veteran skipper Andy McDonald and soon began to dominate play in the middle of the park.

'Big Mac' inspired his younger teammates and dismissed doubts about his fitness by pulling back a goal with a sizzling twenty-five yard strike. Then, mounting another devastating attack, McDonald dribbled his way to the edge of Salthampton's box and Blackie Gray popped up to crash in the equalizer.

With all to play for, it was once more left to Andy McDonald, summoning up every last ounce of energy to produce a sniper-sharp defence splitting pass to put young Roy Race through for a last minute goal and a thrilling come-from-behind victory.

BLACKIE GRAY'S EQUALIZING STRIKE SET UP A STORMING FINISH.

ROVERS ALL AT SEA

Melchester Rovers 2   Hamville 2

Has sentiment at last got the better of Melchester manager Ben Galloway? Judging by skipper Andy McDonald's performance in this tense local derby, the former sailor has become a passenger, not the captain of the Rovers' ship.

In Hamville's very first attack McDonald missed an easy header to concede a gift of a goal. Roy Race valiantly equalized with a crashing drive, only for McDonald, caught napping again, to allow Hamville to regain the lead. Only a last minute equalizer from Blackie Gray saved Melchester from a rotten start to the skipper's last season.

WITH DAZZLING SKILL, ROY SWERVED PAST A CHALLENGING FULL-BACK, AND THEN CRASHED THE BALL PAST THE DIVING GOALIE!

GOAL! GOOD OLD ROY!

WHAT AN EQUALIZER! PLAYED, THE ROVERS!

Buxgate v Melchester Rovers

With a run of fifteen unbeaten games in the bag, Rovers were looking more and more like league champions. With little to fear from their remaining opponents, Rovers' fans were already celebrating the championship. But at snowbound Buxgate, their invincible form went to their heads somewhat.

Three-nil up with just twenty minutes to go, Rovers sat on a cushion of goals from strikers Roy Race (1) and Blackie Gray (2). But they rested on their laurels too long and gave away three goals in a comedy of defensive errors.

Rather than settle for a draw, however, Rovers bounced back thanks to the sheer determination of the brilliant young strikers. Gray, in pain from a serious ankle injury, rifled a perfect centre over to Race...

ROY TRAPPED BLACKIE'S PERFECT CENTRE, AND HIT IT FIRST TIME—

GOAL!!

FOUR-THREE TO ROVERS AND A SIXTEENTH UNBEATEN GAME IN A ROW.

MAY '58

Brookleigh Wanderers v Melchester Rovers

In their toughest test of a tough season, Rovers had an away game at the unbeaten league leaders. The cumulative pressure of the occasion and their long weary season saw Rovers go three goals down by half-time. Not only had the goal-scoring touch of Roy Race and Blackie Gray deserted them, but the defence marshalled by Andy McDonald was leaking goals. The retiring skipper's dream of a league title now seemed to be fast disappearing.

Ben Galloway's gamble on picking his strongest side on paper was looking to have failed. Niggling injuries and fatigue had cost his team chances in the first half. Ben, a shrewd manager, knew that a few well chosen words, at the break, could save the game. As his team trotted out, he had faith in all eleven players. This was a team that could rewrite the Melchester record books...

MELCHESTER ROVERS' LINE UP

1 LEN DOLLAND
2 DAVE WILLIAMS
3 DOUG ROBERTS
4 HUGHIE GRIFFITHS
5 ANDY McDONALD (CAPT.)
6 BUSTER BROWN
7 PIERRE DUPONT
8 BLACKIE GRAY
9 ROY RACE
10 JIM HALLETT
11 TOM DAWSON

FIVE MINUTES AFTER THE RESTART, ANDY McDONALD NEATLY INTERCEPTED A DANGEROUS CENTRE, AND NODDED IT TO INSIDE-RIGHT BLACKIE GRAY

RUNNING ON A FEW YARDS, BLACKIE DREW A DEFENDER OUT OF POSITION, AND THEN PUSHED THE BALL UP TO ROY

ROY SNAPPED UP THE PASS IN A FLASH, AND THE CROWD ROARED AS HE BEAT A BROOKLEIGH BACK AND RACED GOALWARDS

GO ON, ROY! ON YOUR OWN!

LOOK AT HIS SPEED! WHAT A CHANGE FROM THE FIRST HALF!

THE GOALIE RUSHED OUT IN A DESPERATE EFFORT TO PUT ROY OFF, BUT TOO LATE—

GOAL!

SKIPPER ANDY McDONALD RAN ACROSS TO CONGRATULATE ROY—

GOOD WORK, ROY! A FEW MORE SHOTS LIKE THAT AND WE'LL HAVE THE WANDERERS GUESSING!

WE'LL HAVE 'EM LICKED, TOO!

WANDERERS 3 ROVERS 1

WITH THE TITLE BACK WITHIN THEIR REACH, ROVERS MOUNTED A SERIES OF ASSAULTS ON THE BROOKLEIGH GOAL. FROM A CORNER BLACKIE GRAY OUT-JUMPED THE DEFENDERS AND NODDED HOME A SPECTACULAR HEADER TO BRING THE SCORE TO 3-2!

UNDETERRED BY THIS SECOND REVERSE, BROOK-LEIGH, UNBEATEN SINCE EARLY IN THE SEASON SET UP ANOTHER ALL-OUT ATTACK. BUT ANDY WAS PLAYING THE GAME OF HIS LIFE, AND 'THE WANDERERS' FORWARDS WERE BEATEN. THEN ANDY CLEARED THE BALL OUT TO RIGHT-WINGER PIERRE DUPONT.

THE FLYING FRENCHMAN GATHERED THE BALL NEATLY AND STREAKED OFF DOWN THE TOUCHLINE LIKE A GREYHOUND

BROOKLEIGH'S LEFT-HALF POUNDED DESPERATELY AFTER PIERRE, BUT WITH A SUDDEN SWERVE, THE WINGER CHANGED DIRECTION, AND THE RIVAL HALF-BACK PLUNGED HELPLESSLY PAST HIM. NOW PIERRE WAS CLEAR OF OPPOSITION —

NEXT INSTANT, HE SENT OVER A PERFECT CENTRE TO ROY, WHO SLAMMED IT FIRST TIME PAST THE DIVING GOALIE

GOAL! ROVERS HAVE DONE IT! IT'S THE EQUALISER!

IN A SPECIAL ENCLOSURE, THE T.V. COMMENTATOR WAS SHOUTING INTO HIS MIKE, ABOVE THE CHEERING OF THE FANS

AN AMAZING CHANGE HAS COME OVER MELCHESTER IN THIS SECOND HALF, AND IT'S OBVIOUS THAT BROOKLEIGH ARE BADLY SHAKEN! NOW, WITH THE SCORES LEVEL, AND BOTH SIDES FIGHTING ALL THE WAY FOR THE WINNING GOAL, I CAN PROMISE YOU FIREWORKS IN THE LAST FIFTEEN MINUTES!

HOW RIGHT HE WAS! BROOKLEIGH, DETER-MINED NOT TO LOSE THEIR UNBEATEN RECORD, FELL BACK DESPERATELY ON DEFENCE FOR THE LAST FEW MINUTES. ROY LED ATTACK AFTER ATTACK INTO BROOKLEIGH'S GOAL AREA, BUT ROVERS COULD NOT FORCE THE WINNING GOAL. IT LOOKED AS IF THE RESULT WAS TO BE A DRAW. THEN SUDDENLY, AN OVER-ZEALOUS BROOKLEIGH PLAYER TACKLED ROY A LITTLE TOO VIGOROUSLY. THE REF. SIGNALLED A FREE KICK TO ROVERS!

BROOKLEIGH LINED UP TENSELY IN FRONT OF THEIR GOAL, EXPECTING A SHOT. BUT AS ROY RAN UP TO THE BALL, HE DEFTLY FLICKED IT BACK TO ANDY, WHO CRASHED IT FIRST-TIME INTO THE NET —

GOAL!

GOAL!

IT WAS THE SPECTACULAR ENDING TO A THRILL-PACKED GAME, AND AS THE VICTORIOUS ROVERS REACHED THE TOUCHLINE, THE T.V. COMMENTATOR RUSHED ON TO THE FIELD

NO ONE LOOKS MORE DELIGHTED AT THIS SPLENDID ROVERS' WIN THAN THEIR POPULAR SKIPPER, ANDY McDONALD, WHO'S PLAYED THE GREATEST GAME OF HIS CAREER. THE FANS KNOW IT'S HIS LAST SEASON BEFORE RETIRING, AND THEY'RE CHEERING HIM OFF THE FIELD

CONGRATULATIONS ANDY! WHAT A GRAND CLIMAX TO YOUR LAST SEASON! WOULD YOU LIKE TO SAY A FEW WORDS TO YOUR MANY FANS?

YES, I'D LIKE TO TELL EVERYONE THAT THE SUCCESS OF MY LAST SEASON IS LARGELY THANKS TO THE LOYALTY OF ROY AND BLACKIE, WHO HAVE HELPED ME THROUGH SOME TRICKY PERSONAL TROUBLES! NOW I HOPE I CAN LEAD THE ROVERS TO THE LEAGUE CHAMPIONSHIP AT THE SEASON'S CLOSE!

AND SO HE DID. WEEKS LATER, WHEN THE SEASON ENDED, THE ROVERS WERE TOP OF THE LEAGUE. AT THE CELEBRATION DINNER, ROY PRESENTED ANDY WITH A LARGE ALBUM

WE'LL MISS YOU NEXT SEASON, SKIPPER, BUT WE HOPE THIS SCRAP-BOOK, CONTAINING THE HIGHLIGHTS OF YOUR WONDERFUL CAREER, WILL BRING YOU MANY HAPPY MEMORIES

GOSH, THANKS, FELLERS — I DIDN'T EXPECT THIS! BUT YOU HAVEN'T SEEN THE LAST OF ME BY A LONG WAY. I'VE BEEN APPOINTED ASSISTANT-MANAGER, SO I HOPE TO HELP ROVERS TO MANY MORE HONOURS IN THE FUTURE

1957-58

EASY LIES THE HEAD...

AUGUST '58

Following Andy McDonald's retirement, Hughie Griffiths was appointed captain, but Rovers' early season form suffered badly...

Welbeck Wanderers 3   Rovers 2
Rovers 1   Langton United 2
Salthampton 4   Rovers 3
Rovers 1   Tawport United 2

Rovers' fourth defeat in a row saw Griffiths sustain a knee injury, which would keep him out of the game for months to come. In light of the growing crisis, chairman Mr Mason called a meeting of the directors and Roy Race was requested to appear before them...

Asked for his response to being appointed captain, Roy told the Gazette, "I'm chuffed, I feel like Sputnik, over the moon!"

SEPTEMBER '58

In his first game as captain against league leaders Bamford Athletic, Roy had the added responsibility of overseeing the debuts of two players new to Rovers' first team. Tubby Morton, in goal, and Dick Stokes, a lively right-winger.

Tubby's inexperience soon showed as he conceded two soft goals. A converted centre-half, Tubby was trying too hard to impress his manager. As a rout seemed on the cards, Tubby regained his nerve and was showing his true colours. With his new 'keeper back in control, Roy turned his attention to attack – with spectacular results. Three quick goals turned the tide and Rovers seemed poised to win.

However, in injury time, a harmless looking Bamford cross floated into Tubby's penalty area and Blackie Gray, back defending, swung a foot at the ball...

FINAL SCORE – MELCHESTER ROVERS 3   BAMFORD ATH. 3

ROVERS SET OUT ON THE ROAD TO WEMBLEY

FA Cup 3rd Round
Melchester Rovers 3   Elbury Wanderers 0

There's something in the air around Melchester Stadium this season and it's not just the lingering 'aroma' from the pickle works. It's the sweet smell of cup success.

Rovers may only be tenth in the league, but maybe that is just a sign that a thrilling cup run is in the offing. Not since the golden days of '38 have Melchester scarves graced the terraces of Wembley. Too often they have stumbled at the first hurdle of the Third Round, becoming Goliaths to teams of lesser stature and fuelling talk of a cup jinx. But against a classy Elbury side, Rovers displayed the polish of cup winners. First Race, as inspirational as ever, with a header in the very first minute of the game, then Gray, leaping like a salmon, to volley home, gave Rovers a two-goal lead at half-time.

Race scored again, driving home the final blow in the second minute of injury time with a superb header.

JANUARY '59

FA Cup 4th Round
Melchester Rovers v Portdean City

Roy Race knew Rovers must defeat 'the Deaners' at Melchester Stadium and not risk a replay away to a team unbeaten at home all season. Current league champions they may have been, but in cup pedigree, Rovers were the underdogs and this eased the pressure on them.

Rovers struck early with lightning speed. One minute into the game Portdean moved swiftly into top gear and were soon attacking Rovers' goal. But Roy Race cleared the ball from defence, finding winger Dick Stokes who unleashed a pass to Blackie Gray. A perfect cross found Roy's head. One-nil to Rovers.

But Rovers seemed to freeze in the second half. Portdean took a two-one lead and Rovers' lynch-pin half-back Buster Brown suffered concussion in a desperate tackle and was out cold. Rovers' cup run was spluttering to a halt.

Then Race made a monumental decision. He put Stokes in goal and sent young goalkeeper Tubby Morton to his position at right wing! It proved a stroke of genius. Morton, a former centre-half, was soon pounding down the wing, crossing to Gray, who drove in the equalizer with just two minutes to go.

Just seconds before the final whistle, Stokes found Morton with a gigantic up-field punt, Morton whipped in a cross that seemed to be beyond Roy Race's powers of retrieval...

ROVERS WERE THROUGH TO THE FIFTH ROUND

FEBRUARY '59

FA Cup 5th Round
Carnbrook Town v Melchester Rovers

Two-nil down to Third division Carnbrook Town it looked like Melchester would once more fall victim to the FA Cup giant-killers. But Roy Race's half-time pep talk really did the trick.

A quick goal from Race sent Carnbrook reeling, a second from Blackie Gray left them stunned and powerless. Sensing victory Melchester swept forward in attack after attack. It wasn't long before Race slammed home Rovers' third goal – and just before the end...

FINAL SCORE –
MELCHESTER ROVERS 4   CARNBROOK TOWN 2

MARCH '59

FA Cup 6th Round
Melchester Rovers v Bronton City

With skilful skipper Roy Race on top form, Rovers looked unstoppable in the cup. Off the pace in the League hunt, they were throwing their all in for cup glory. Against Bronton City, Rovers were majestic; tireless in attack, solid in defence. Race completed his hat-trick, his second in succession, to take Rovers into the semi-finals.

APRIL '59

FA Cup semi-final
Melchester Rovers v Brampton United

Following a coach accident on the way to the semi-final at Sandower Stadium, a ruffled Rovers' side were off form. In a terrible start, Rovers' right-back Dave Williams panicked in defence and sent the ball into his own net!

Trailing one-nil Rovers appeared even more rattled and Dave Williams, desperately trying to make up for his error, late-tackled Brampton's number ten, Len Jones and gave away a penalty. Was this the end of Rovers' glorious cup run?

When Tubby Morton, Rovers' new goalie hurled himself headlong to save the penalty, it looked like Rovers' luck might have changed. After the break, inside right Jim Hallett jinked his way through the Brampton defence and slipped a perfect pass to Roy Race...

Although Brampton's defenders played like supermen, Rovers were really on their toes now. With only a few minutes left, Roy Race sent the ball crashing into Brampton's net from a free kick on the edge of the penalty area. Rovers were through to a Wembley Cup Final and Roy Race, with eight goals in three matches, was the man they had to thank.

1959 FA CUP FINAL

Melchester Rovers v Langton United

at Wembley Stadium

As if Rovers wouldn't have enough to contend with against Langton in the final, Ted Smith, sworn enemy of Melchester Rovers was determined to prevent them from winning the cup by any means! Roy and Blackie had been cast adrift in a boat off Portsea by Smith and had still not arrived at Wembley as manager Ben Galloway gave his pre-match team-talk....

NEXT MOMENT, THE MANAGER BROKE OFF AS THE DOOR WAS FLUNG OPEN!

ROY—BLACKIE! YOU'RE HERE!

WHERE'VE YOU TWO BEEN? WHAT HAPPENED?

NO TIME TO EXPLAIN NOW, GUV'NOR! CHEER UP, LADS! WE'LL BE WITH YOU IN A MINUTE!

A FEW MINUTES LATER THE MIGHTY STADIUM ROCKED TO A THUNDEROUS ROAR AS THE TWO TEAMS TOOK THE FIELD!

HERE THEY COME! GOOD OLD ROY! ROVERS FOR THE CUP!

HOORAY! SHOW 'EM, LANGTON! WE WANT GOALS!

WHEN THE TEAMS MARCHED TO THE FRONT OF THE STAND, TED SMITH COULDN'T BELIEVE HIS OWN EYES!

HOW THE HECK DID THEY ESCAPE AND GET HERE IN TIME? THEY KNOW I TRAPPED THEM — THEY'LL TELL THE COPS! I MUST GET AWAY SOMEHOW!

AT LAST, THE PRELIMINARIES OVER, THE GREAT MATCH STARTED——

LANGTON UNITED SWUNG STRAIGHT INTO A POWERFUL ATTACK, AND THE ROVERS WERE DRIVEN BACK. IT WAS QUICKLY OBVIOUS, TOO, THAT ROY AND BLACKIE WERE FEELING THE EFFECTS OF THEIR TIRING ORDEAL

ROY FEELS LIKE I DO — FLAKED OUT!

THEN, AFTER ONLY A FEW MINUTES' PLAY, THE ROVERS WERE A GOAL DOWN!

GOAL!

FROM THEN ON, THE ROVERS SETTLED DOWN AND BEGAN TO ATTACK, BUT ROY MISSED ONE GLORIOUS CHANCE————

UNDETERRED, THE ROVERS FLUNG EVERYTHING INTO THEIR ATTACKS, BUT WITHOUT MUCH LUCK. AND THEN, JUST BEFORE HALF-TIME, LANGFORD SCORED AGAIN!

THEY'VE DONE IT AGAIN! UP, UNITED!

POOR OLD ROVERS! THEY'VE HAD IT NOW!

WHEN THE GRIM-FACED ROVERS RETURNED TO THE DRESSING-ROOM AT HALF-TIME, MR. MASON, THE CLUB CHAIRMAN, WAS WAITING——

BAD LUCK, ROY! YOU AND BLACKIE ARE FEELING THE EFFECTS OF YOUR DASH TO GET HERE

YOU'RE RIGHT THERE, SIR. BUT I GUESS WE'RE LUCKY TO BE HERE AT ALL AFTER WHAT HAPPENED TO US. I'D LIKE TO GET MY HANDS ON THAT SO-CALLED SUPPORTER OF OURS — TED SMITH!

SO WOULD I——— LEND ME THAT PENKNIFE, ROY!

SUDDENLY MR. MASON GRABBED ROY'S HAND———

I'D KNOW THIS KNIFE ANYWHERE — IT BELONGS TO A CHAUFFEUR OF MINE. I SACKED HIM FOR STEALING! WHERE DID YOU GET IT, ROY?

IT WAS DROPPED IN THE SUPPORTERS' CLUB WEEKS AGO BY THE CHAP WE NOW KNOW AS TED SMITH — THE MAN RESPONSIBLE FOR ALL OUR TROUBLES!

I SEE IT NOW. TO GET HIS REVENGE ON ME FOR SACKING HIM, SMITH HAS TRIED TO RUIN ROVERS CHANCE OF WINNING THE CUP!

WELL, HE WON'T SUCCEED! WE'RE TWO DOWN, LADS, BUT WE'RE GOING OUT THERE AGAIN — TO WIN!

Melchester Rovers Line Up

1
TUBBY MORTON

2
DAVE WILLIAMS

3
BOB ROBERTS

4
HUGHIE GRIFFITHS

5
PADDY RYAN

6
BUSTER BROWN

8
BLACKIE GRAY

10
JIM HALLETT

7
DICK STOKES

9
ROY RACE (CAPT.)

11
TOM DAWSON

MANAGER BEN GALLOWAY'S HALF-TIME TEAM TALK SOON HAD ITS EFFECT IN THE SECOND-HALF....

ROVERS 1   UNITED 2

28

1959 F.A. CUP FINAL ROVERS WERE RIGHT BACK IN THE GAME AGAIN, AND, ROARED ON BY THEIR JUBILANT FANS, THEY BATTERED AT THE LANGTON GOAL

UP, ROVERS! YOU'VE GOT 'EM GROGGY!

WELL SAVED, THE GOALIE!

THE T.V. COMMENTATOR WAS GETTING AS EXCITED AS THE GREAT CROWD —

THE ROVERS ARE RIGHT BACK. TO THEIR OLD FORM NOW — ROY RACE IS PLAYING A TERRIFIC GAME, AND LANGTON ARE DEFENDING DESPERATELY. — RACE IS THROUGH AGAIN — WHAT A PLAYER! — HE'S BEING TACKLED — NO — HE'S PASSED TO STOKES ON THE RIGHT-WING AND — — —

NEXT MOMENT, THE MIGHTY STADIUM ROCKED WITH THE THUNDEROUS ROAR THAT GREETED ROVERS' SECOND GOAL —

DICK — WHAT A GOAL! WE'RE LEVEL!

BRAVO, LADS! NOW COME ON — WE CAN DO IT! JUST ONE MORE AND THE CUP'S OURS!

BUT ONE MELCHESTER "SUPPORTER" DIDN'T SEE THAT GOAL! HE WAS TED SMITH, FORMER CHAUFFEUR OF ROVERS' CHAIRMAN, MR. MASON, WHO HAD SWORN TO STOP ROY AND CO. WINNING THE CUP. THE POLICE HAD CAUGHT UP WITH HIM!

I HAD TO SACK HIM FOR STEALING FROM ME — SO HE TRIED TO GET HIS REVENGE BY ATTACKING THE TEAM! TAKE HIM AWAY — I'LL BE ALONG TO CHARGE HIM AFTER I'VE SEEN ROVERS WIN THE CUP!

WHEN MR. MASON RETURNED TO HIS SEAT, ONLY A FEW MINUTES REMAINED FOR PLAY, AND THE SCORES WERE STILL LEVEL. THEN ROVERS WERE AWARDED A FREE-KICK JUST OUTSIDE THE PENALTY AREA — —

THIS IS OUR LAST CHANCE — WE CAN'T RISK EXTRA TIME!

BUSTER BROWN TOOK THE FREE-KICK, BUT INSTEAD OF TRYING A SHOT, HE LOBBED THE BALL OVER THE BUNCHED DEFENDERS AND — —

ROY AND THE LANGTON GOALIE FLUNG THEMSELVES AT THE BALL, BUT IT WAS ROY'S FOOT THAT GOT TO IT FIRST! NEXT MOMENT — — —

IT'S THERE! ROY — YOU'VE DONE IT!

IT WAS THE END! MELCHESTER ROVERS HAD WON THE CUP!

WELL DONE, ROY! YOU DESERVE IT!

THANKS, BILL! YOU GAVE US A GREAT GAME!

WHAT A RECEPTION THE FANS GAVE THE ROVERS AS ROY LED THEM UP TO THE ROYAL BOX — — —

GOOD OLD, ROY!

UP THE ROVERS! WHAT A TEAM!

IT WAS THE PROUDEST MOMENT OF ROY'S LIFE WHEN HE TURNED TO SHOW THE WILDLY CHEERING FANS THE GLEAMING SILVER TROPHY—

BACK ON THE FAMOUS WEMBLEY PITCH, ROY AND THE TRIUMPHANT ROVERS FACED A BATTERY OF CAMERAS AND MICROPHONES — — —

GOSH, I'M THE HAPPIEST CHAP IN BRITAIN TO-DAY! I'M PROUD TO BE SKIPPER OF THE 'FINEST BUNCH OF LADS IN FOOTBALL!

THE END

YOUNG GUNS SHOOT-TO-THRILL POLICY!

DECEMBER '59

Following a gruelling pre-season tour of Italy, Rovers stumbled at the start of the season, losing touch with the early leaders Salthampton and Elbury Wanderers.

Better things started happening on the pitch when Rovers recovered from a two goal deficit against Brymouth City, inspired by Roy Race's amazing full-length diving header, which levelled the scores, Roy had also netted with Rovers' first. Rovers settled matters with a late goal from mystery player "Ralph". The player of exceptional ability appeared from nowhere unable to account for his past, only remembering his christian name. What was not mysterious about this player was his uncanny ball control and understanding of the game for one so young.

Rovers' next league game, away against Tedbury Athletic, saw them continue their meteoric rise up the division. The final 5-1 scoreline flattered the home side as Rovers ran rampant and looked forward to challenging for another league championship.

By year end, Rovers had recovered sufficiently to be in touch with new league leaders Portdean City. Trailing the leaders by just four points, Rovers started the New Year in determined mood against lowly Carlington City.

New boy at inside-right Ken Harcombe, had replaced Blackie Gray, who'd been badly injured when the Melchester Stadium dressing rooms had burnt down over the Christmas break. Harcombe was an instant success with two late goals to give Rovers a three-two come-from-behind win, against Carlington City. Roy Race continued his goal-a-game average with a spectacularly taken overhead kick to set Rovers on their way to another comeback victory, that was becoming a mark of their season.

With Blackie Gray in hospital, under sedation, under police guard and under suspicion for the arson attack on the Rovers' dressing rooms, Roy Race tried desperately to clear his young friend's good name. Roy had other problems to sort out at the club, since all the other Rovers' players blamed the arson attack on newcomer Harcombe, though Roy wasn't so quick to jump to conclusions. His own investigations suggested others may have been involved and vowed to clear the names of both Rovers' inside-rights.

Before Roy could act any further in the matter, that was beginning to split the team apart with accusation and counter-claim, he had to play in a special Monday night game against crack Austrian visitors Flaudermitz.

Roy knew that keeping his team together against such skilful visitors would be no easy task, but he was more concerned with extinguishing the rumours surrounding the arson attack.

Since the accusations against Ken Harcombe had done much to undermine the team spirit, manager Ben Galloway delayed naming his eleven until only minutes before the kick-off, in an attempt to concentrate his players' minds on the game at hand.

As Galloway and Roy were making their final decision on the team's line-up, the door of the board-room – being used as a makeshift dressing room – burst open to reveal a bedraggled Blackie Gray.

Blackie explained that he had checked out of hospital and was fully fit to play. Sensing the return of their star forward might galvanise the team into a solid performance Galloway named both Gray and Harcombe in the team.

What Blackie had not fully explained to his manager, captain or team-mates was that he had given his police guard the slip at the hospital and would be arrested at any minute.

But first he knew he had a game to win...

DIVISION ONE – TOP FOUR

	P	W	D	L	F	A	Pts
Portdean City	22	16	5	1	55	12	37
Salthampton	22	15	5	2	50	20	35
Elbury Wanderers	22	16	2	4	45	24	34
Melchester Rovers	22	14	5	3	51	27	33

ROY JUST MANAGED TO BEAT THE AUSTRIAN TO IT ... AND THE BALL ZIPPED PAST THE GOALIE'S FINGERS ... INTO THE NET ...

ROVERS 1
FLAUDERMITZ 0

ROY WAS MOBBED BY HIS BACK-SLAPPING TEAM-MATES, BUT AS HE PARTED FROM THEM, BLACKIE GRAY SPOKE TENSELY ...

SORRY I FLUFFED MY SHOT, ROY. I SEEM TO BE A BIT OFF-TARGET ...

I KNOW WHAT'S WRONG WITH YOU, BLACKIE. YOU'RE WORRIED ABOUT THE POLICE ... COMING HERE TO ARREST YOU !

Roy had hit the nail right on the head !

Recently, a mysterious fire had broken out in the Rovers' dressing room, completely destroying it.

Evidence was found which seemed to prove that Blackie Gray was responsible for starting the blaze, and the police were keeping him under observation in hospital.

Roy was convinced that his pal was innocent, and was determined to help clear his name.

But Blackie had given the cops the slip to come and play in this match, and Roy realised it was only a matter of time before they turned up at the Stadium—probably, to arrest him during the game !

FROM THE RESTART, THE AUSTRIANS LAUNCHED ATTACK AFTER ATTACK ... UNTIL AT LAST THEIR CENTRE FORWARD BROKE THROUGH, WITH ONLY THE GOALIE TO BEAT ... HE SHOT !

MIKE DRURY, SUBSTITUTING AS GOALIE FOR TUBBY MORTON, WHO HAD FLU, SEEMED ONLY TO GET ONE HAND TO THE BALL. IT SPUN TOWARDS THE GOAL ... WITH THE AUSTRIAN CENTRE RACING AFTER IT ...

... THEN A RED STREAK TORE IN ... ROY RACE ... DESPERATELY OUT TO SAVE WHAT SEEMED A CERT GOAL !

THE CROWD HELD ITS BREATH WITH HEART-STOPPING SUSPENSE.

WOW! WHAT A SPRINT !

HE CAN'T GET IT ... YES, HE CAN ! HE HAS !

WELL CLEARED, ROY !

SOME TIME AFTER THAT, ROY GOT POSSESSION AND SENT A LONG PASS OUT TO BLACKIE. BUT HIS PAL COMPLETELY IGNORED THE BALL.

HEY ! WHAT'S WRONG WITH BLACKIE ? MY STARS ! THE POLICE ! THEY'RE HERE IN FORCE ... PROBABLY TO ARREST HIM !

BUT ROY HAD NO TIME TO WORRY ANY MORE ABOUT BLACKIE. HE BECAME INVOLVED IN A FIERCE SCRIMMAGE ...

... AND A RIVAL PLAYER'S SWINGING BOOT CAUGHT HIM ACCIDENTALLY ON THE SIDE OF THE HEAD ...

ROY LAY ON THE GROUND, COMPLETELY K.O.'ED. THE REF. ANXIOUSLY CALLED TAFF MORGAN ON TO THE FIELD ...

GET YOUR MAN OFF THE FIELD TO ATTEND TO HIM, TRAINER. WE CAN'T HOLD UP PLAY WHILE YOU DO IT HERE.

A FEW MOMENTS LATER, THE CROWD SAW THE SAD SIGHT OF ROY BEING CARRIED OFF ON A STRETCHER ...

THERE GOES POOR OLD ROY ! GOSH, THAT'S HARD LUCK ON THE ROVERS !

THEY'LL NEVER HOLD FLAUDERMITZ WITH ONLY TEN MEN !

IN THE TEMPORARY DRESSING-ROOM, ROY SOON CAME TO UNDER THE MINISTRATIONS OF TAFF MORGAN. HE SAT UP AND BLINKED AT THE CLOCK.

YOW! ONLY FIVE MINUTES TO HALF-TIME ! THEN BLACKIE WILL COME OFF THE FIELD AND BE ARRESTED. I'VE GOT TO DO SOMETHING ABOUT IT ... QUICK !

BULLSEYE!!

In true fashion, after the arrest of Reg Murphy and his accomplice reserve goalkeeper Mike Drury, a relieved Blackie Gray scored Rovers' second goal after the break to defeat Flaudermitz two-nil.

Rovers' form in the league kept them well in touch with Portdean, as they turned their attention to the first leg of their International Club Cup Quarter-final against South America's San Angino. An equalizer by Roy Race in injury time saw Rovers fly out to South America for the second leg in high spirits.

FEBRUARY '60

ROVERS VANISH!

No trace has yet been found of the British Transatlantic Air Services aircraft which was taking First Division team Melchester Rovers to their football game in San Angino. A full-scale search is underway, but their seems little hope of any survivors.

MAR '60   TELEGRAM

To: BELTIGUAN GOVERNMENT

From: BRITISH TRANSATLANTIC AIR SERVICES

BELIEVE BRITISH AIRCRAFT CARRYING MELCHESTER ROVERS FOOTBALL TEAM CRASH LANDED ON BELTIGUA.

\<Stop\>

VITAL THEY ARE FOUND

\<Stop\>

PLEASE INVESTIGATE AND REPORT

\<Ends\>

MARCH '60

ROVERS SAFE!

Tales of kidnap and football games in the jungle.

Out of the powder blue tropic sky a plane landed and off limped the missing Melchester Rovers team – looking like they had been in a war-zone. They had - the Beltiguan civil war. With their airplane shot down by rebel forces, Rovers were lucky to escape the crash-landing. The team were forced to march through jungle and swamp to a football pitch marked out in the jungle. Two games against a rebel team, either side of a failed escape attempt, left Rovers bruised, battered and bewildered.

With the second leg of the I.C.C. only twenty four hours away, a semi-final berth does not look likely.

MARCH '60 PROGRAMME NOTES V BRONTON

As you might have already read in your newspapers, Rovers had an adventure on their visit to South America. Fortunately, in the end, everything turned out alright, except we lost the International Club Cup game against San Angino and bowed out of the competition. I wish San Angino all the best – they were the better team on the day – for their forthcoming semi-final.

In light of our equatorial escapade, the Football League have kindly allowed us to postpone the league matches we missed while we were indisposed. This means we have a lot of catching up with Portdean, now ten points clear of us. Let's hope we can win our five games in hand...

ROY RACE

MAY '60

CHAMPIONSHIP SHOWDOWN!

In their last game of the season, Rovers travelled to Portdean City for the title clincher – knowing a win would see them return to Melchester in style as League Champions – again! For those fans who could not get to Portdean, the game could be heard live on Radio

MAY '60

RADIO MELCHESTER COMMENTARY

"Welcome to Portdean Stadium on a typical MAY day. Portdean MAY take the League title and so MAY visitors Melchester Rovers....

"...That's the Portdean line-up, wearing their famous blue and gold stripes with white shorts. And now the visiting Rovers' team – 1. Tubby Morton 2. Dave Williams 3. Doug Roberts 4. Hugh Griffiths 5. Paddy Ryan 6. Buster Brown 7. Dick Stokes 8. Blackie Gray 9. Roy Race 10. Jim Hallett 11. Tom Dawson. Rovers wearing red shirts with yellow collar and blue shorts will kick-off from our right and defend the Dean Street end. The question is will the rigours of this difficult season begin to tell on this plucky Rovers' team, who have played and won six games in the last fifteen days. We shall find out, as referee Mr Brown gets the game underway..."

"...Thirty-five minutes gone here at Portdean and the home side are still leading 1-0 thanks to a well-taken goal from winger Ted Anderson. Rovers have had most of the play up until now but cannot break down this determined 'Dean defence.

Throw in on the left to Rovers, the ball is played in by Hallett, nodded on by Gray to Race who turns inside the area. Brought down by Cargill! "No!" says referee Brown and waves play on...the ball runs away to Dawson. He lets fly. Oh dear! High, wide and – A GOAL! Roy Race picked himself off the floor and lunged at the ball as it flashed wildly across the goal. He got his head to Dawson's mishit shot and has levelled the scores. Well, well. You can't keep a man like Roy Race down for too long. Denied a penalty he managed to turn the play to his advantage."

"Only a few seconds to go in this match and Portdean will settle for the draw, which will be enough to see them crowned League Champions. Rovers have stuck manfully to their task but they have finally run out of steam and out of ideas.

Maybe one last chance here. Gray picks up the ball in the inside-right position, he goes past one defender and plays a wall-pass with Race. Rovers are threatening. Gray strings out a long ball to Stokes on the right-wing. Stokes back inside to Race who sets off on a bulling run at the heart of the Portdean defence. Avoids one tackler, goes past another...No! Brought down inside the box. This time the referee has no hesitation in pointing to the spot. Race is still down and the Rovers' players rush over to their fallen captain. Race is the Rovers' penalty-taker and this spot-kick could mean so much. My watch shows ninety minutes is up. If Rovers' score they would be Champions.

On his feet, Race walks calmly over to the ball on the penalty spot, picks the ball up and wipes a piece of dirt from it. Places the ball down with the precision of a master craftsman and looks up at Ernie Wilson in Portdean's goal. The posts must seem to be inching in as Race surveys the scene before him. Rovers' fans behind the goal can't bear to look, nor can the Rovers' players. Race has walked back five yards and begins his angled run. He must be going to the keeper's left, he shoots, the keeper dives to his left and the ball...the ball swerves viciously off the edge of Roy's boot and buries itself in the top right hand corner of the net. Three-two to Rovers and Roy Race has fooled us all again! There goes the whistle and Rovers are League Champions for the second time in three seasons."

HOME IS WHERE THE HEART GROWS STRONGER

ROVERS LOOK FORWARD TO NEW SEASON WITH HOPE!

League Champions Melchester Rovers returned home from their successful tour of Italy to face a more local challenge. Second Division champions and neighbours Shermall Athletic's first appearance in the First Division will add extra bite to the cross-town rivalry. A fact Rovers' captain Roy Race acknowledges, "With Shermall breathing down our necks from across the river, we won't be able to rest up for a minute. Apart from being great news for the city, two teams in the top flight means we can't sit back on our laurels nor will we count our chickens before they come home to roost."

BUBBLE BURSTS FOR ROVERS

Kestow United 3   Melchester Rovers 0

Six games into the defence of their League crown and Rovers have yet to win a game. The latest humiliation, a three goal drubbing by Kestow, leaves Rovers one place off the bottom of the league. Meanwhile First Division newcomers Shermall Athletic are enjoying a purple patch – undefeated in their first six games.

The two teams meet at Shermall Stadium in two weeks and another Rovers' defeat could spell an early end to their league season.

Division One League table – Bottom four

	P	W	D	L	F	A	Pts
Darnsley	6	1	2	3	8	8	4
Granton United	6	1	2	3	7	10	4
Melchester Rovers	6	0	3	3	4	13	3
Motspur Town	6	0	2	4	4	15	2

ROY RACE DOES IT ALL!

Shermall Athletic 1   Melchester Rovers 4

What can't Roy Race do on a football field? Having scored twice himself, he then set up Jim Hallett for a third before half-time. Race was on the receiving end of some rough-house tactics from the hosts and limped out of the game. An unfortunate injury to Tubby Morton as he tried valiantly to stop Shermall's opening goal, saw the goalkeeper stretchered off to be replaced between the posts by the badly limping Race. Within seconds the stand-in 'keeper made a diving save to thwart Jackson, as Shermall looked to pull another goal back. Forgetting his new position, Race shrugged off his leg injury and shrugged off the whole of the Shermall side, as he dribbled the ball over halfway. On the edge of the area, he froze, as though remembering his defensive responsibilities. But a swift shimmy took him past the last defender and Race beat his opposite number from fifteen yards out.

In one movement Roy Race had kick-started Rovers spluttering season. It may be too late to repeat their League triumph of last year, but Rovers can set their sights firmly on the F.A. Cup.

NEW HOME FOR ROVERS

TO BE TRANSFERRED TO SHERMALL STADIUM ATHLETIC WILL MOVE TO ROVERS' GROUND

In a shock announcement, Lance Vigors – chairman of Shermall Athletic – has bought the controlling interest in Melchester Rovers from former chairman John Mason, whose department store empire is in financial trouble and was forced to make a quick sale.

Vigors has invested thousands of pounds in turning Shermall into a Division One side, and in building a fine new stadium. How this will effect the two teams, who now swap grounds, can only be gauged on the football field.

NIGHTMARE ON MEL STREET

Melchester Rovers 1   Portdean City 4

Rovers' dream start to their first game at their new home quickly turned into a nightmare. One goal up from a well-worked Blackie Gray free-kick, Rovers were coasting at half-time. Inspired by the palatial surroundings of Shermall Stadium, Rovers played like princes in the first forty-five minutes. The second half was a different matter. A freak goal saw the ball rebound off the post, hit goalkeeper Tubby Morton and drop over the line for the equalizer. This seemed to knock the stuffing out of Rovers. Three more goals from the visitors turned the tables and Rovers went down to their biggest home defeat for five years.

FIRE AT SHERMALL STADIUM

ROVERS RETURN TO MEL PARK

A mystery fire at Shermall Stadium has closed the ground down indefinitely. Melchester Rovers have been forced to switch this weekend's Third round F.A. Cup match back to Mel Park.

Rovers are in need of some good news having failed to win at their new home in five matches. Last week's three-nil defeat by Kestow United (the second such scoreline of the season) has prompted their chairman Lance Vigors to announce that captain Roy Race's future is in doubt.

If Rovers fail to win the F.A. Cup – Roy Race could well be on his way out of Melchester. How Roy reacts to this news will be another test of his character. Ever since Vigors took over at Rovers, the two men have not seen eye-to-eye...maybe it's time for Roy to say good-bye!

1960/61 FA CUP RESULTS

JAN '61 – 3rd Round
Melchester Rovers 1   Charnley Athletic 0
Race

JAN '61 – 4th Round
Portdean City 1   Melchester Rovers 2
Gray, Race

FEB '61 – 5th Round
Baxgate 2   Melchester Rovers 2
Race (2)

Replay
Melchester Rovers 4   Baxgate 1
Race, Gray (2), Pike

MAR '61 – 6th Round
Melchester Rovers 3   Bronton City 0
Race (3)

Draw for the F.A. Cup Semi-finals
Corstone City v Eastoke United
Melchester Rovers v Shermall Athletic!!

REALISING THAT THE EVIDENCE AGAINST HIM WAS VERY STRONG, STENNING DECIDED TO COME CLEAN, "OKAY – YOU WIN. DARN YOU RACE! IT'S ALL TRUE. I'M BANKING ON ROVERS GETTING THROUGH TO WEMBLEY SO I CAN WRITE IN MY COLUMN *STENNING – THE ONLY WRITER TO TIP ROVERS TO REACH THE CUP FINAL!* IF THEY FAIL, I'LL GET THE SACK – SO I HAD TO DO SOMETHING."

THE OPPOSING TEAMS HANDED STENNING OVER TO THE AUTHORITIES AND TOOK THE PITCH FOR THE SECOND HALF, WITH A PLACE AT WEMBLEY STILL VERY MUCH AT STAKE....

"Ten minutes gone in the second half, Rovers pile on the pressure looking for an equalizer. Winger Dick Stokes has forced a corner on the left, and will take it himself.
The Rovers fans – to a man are lifting their team. Stokes swings a long ball into the penalty area. Up goes Race.
He's knocked down by the keeper who half punches the ball to the edge of the area. The ball falls to Gray – takes aim, let's fly – HITS THE POST!!
The ball comes back into play, Race – on the ground – lashes out a foot at the rebound and...."

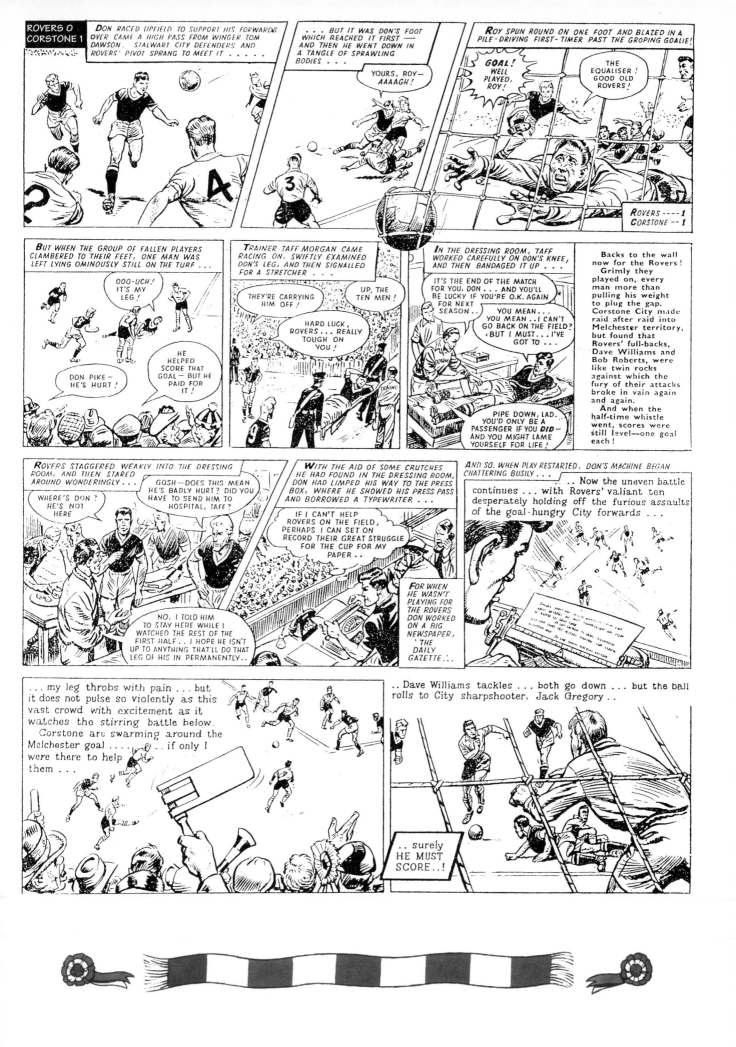

DON PIKE'S
FINGERS FROZE
MOMENTARILY
OVER HIS TYPE-
WRITER – HIS
HEART THUMP-
ING IN HIS
MOUTH.
SUDDENLY HIS
FINGERS WERE
NO LONGER PART
OF HIM, THEY
TYPED FRANTI-
CALLY AS IF
INSPIRED BY A
UNKNOWN
FORCE...

"...City centre-forward
has the ball...the
goal is wide open...
...HE
SHOOTS..."

"...the ball
screams for
the net...
...Rovers' diving
goalie misses it...
...it's a goal...
it must be!..."

"...but NO! A flying figure in red
streaks across...boots it clear..."

SAVED!

GOOD
OLD
ROY!

...it's Rovers' skipper Roy Race...
....he's come to the rescue of his
harassed defence...what a
player!......

"...now Rovers' skipper goes
down the wing on one of his
celebrated do-or-die solo dashes..."

COME
ON,
ROY!

GO IT, YOU
ROVERS!

..outside right Dick Stokes moves over
to the centre to be ready for a pass...

...Roy cleverly outwits a City defender...over
goes his centre..Dick Stokes
takes a first time slam...

...but the Corstone back's out-
thrust foot has deflected the ball!..
...just that fraction...WHAM!
It hits the crossbar..and rebounds..

OOOOOH!
MISSED!

HARD LUCK,
DICK!

...right into the path of
Roy Race, who flings himself
headlong forward like an
aerial torpedo in full flight...

GOAL!
GOAL!

WHAT
A SMASHING
SHOT!

...it's there! It's in the net!
Incredibly the ten men from
Melchester have snatched
the lead from the
full-strength City!

ROVERS 2
CORSTONE 1

Even a fluent writer
such as Don Pike found
that words could hardly
describe the thrills that
followed as Corstone
City flung everything
they had into trying to
regain level footing.
But Rovers' gallant ten
were inspired by a
feverish determination
that made them work
football wonders which
will never be forgotten!
And when at last,
without either side scor-
ing again, the ref's
whistle shrilled for full
time, the whole of
Wembley trembled to a
shock-wave of cheering
that nearly lifted the
domes from the two
great towers!
Don Pike wound up hi
report:

...now comes the
proudest moment for Roy
Race...when he receives
the magnificent trophy..
...and is borne aloft by
his triumphant team-
mates...

WE'VE DONE
IT, CHAPS! THE
CUP'S OURS
AT LAST!

MOSTLY
THANKS
TO YOU,
ROY!

...and I must take my crutches and limp back
back to the dressing room to meet them all...

MAY '61 – DIVISION ONE LEAGUE TABLE – BOTTOM FOUR								
	P	W	D	L	F	A	Pts	Goal Diff
Granton Utd	42	9	12	21	39	67	30	-28
Railford Town	42	8	14	20	34	62	30	-28
Melchester Rovers	40	8	10	22	30	63	26	-33
Darnsley	42	5	15	22	27	75	25	-48

Rovers must win their last
two league games – by five
goals – to avoid relegation...

Rovers 2 Hamville 0
Gray (2)

Storeford Athletic 1 Rovers 4
Morton (og) *Race (3), Hallett*

MAY '61

ROVERS ESCAPE
RELEGATION – BY
ONE GOAL

ANY PORT IN A STORM IN A CUP-RUN!

ROVERS STARTED THE NEW SEASON, IN THE NEW LOOK MEL PARK STADIUM AGAINST EASTOKE. ROY AND THE TEAM WERE LOOKING FORWARD TO ROVER'S FIRST SEASON OF EUROPEAN COMPETITION.

ITALIAN CLUB STADIA BATORI MADE A TRANSFER OFFER OF £85,000 FOR ROY RACE, BUT THE ROVERS' CAPTAIN MADE IT CLEAR THAN HE INTENDS TO STAY AT MELCHESTER, "I WOULDN'T LEAVE MELCHESTER FOR ALL THE MONEY IN CHINA. I'M LOOKING FORWARD TO FACING WELLINGFORD THIS WEEK."

JANUARY '62 PROGRAMME NOTES v CORSTONE CITY

"Rovers bid farewell to popular centre half Paddy Ryan – who has decided it's time to move on, but not to Italy. Paddy, too, is not to be tempted by the lure of the lire, he will take over from former Rovers' captain Andy McDonald as Principal at Spartan House Sports School. Andy is to become manager of his old club Langton Town, now in the Third Division. All our wishes go out to two great Rovers' stalwarts.

Paddy's place will be filled by Ossie Jones – a six foot six inch centre-half from the Rhondda Valley. Ossie joins us at a critical time, as we prepare to face Schonved in our first venture into Europe."

ROY RACE

The Equalizer?....

MARCH '62

FA Cup 5th Round
Melchester Rovers 3   Stanport Rangers 4

Rovers took their leave of the F.A. Cup in a thrilling fifth round tie. Three times, through Gray, Race and Jones, Rovers came from behind to peg back a Rangers side that now reach the Sixth round for the first time in a dozen years.

Jinx or no jinx – Rovers' season is now over. Having been hustled out the Cup Winners' Cup by Schonved. Rovers' league position, though creditably placed mid-table, in view of last season's last ditch salvage operation, means there is nothing to play for.

IF THE ENGLAND CAP FITS, WEAR IT...

AUGUST '62

WINNING START FOR ROVERS
EXPLOSIVE START FOR REEVES

Melchester Rovers 4   Cashford Albion 0

Following a record-breaking tour of Australia, Rovers started the domestic league season at a record pace. A four-nothing demolition of Cashford Albion set Rovers' title challenge off on the right foot. It was Roy Race's left foot though, that notched Rovers' first league goal of the new season and a cracker it was too. Three more goals for Hallett, Gray and Race sealed victory.

Making his debut for Rovers in this game was right-half Albert "Bomber" Reeves – aptly described as "The Hardest Head in Football" for his superior heading ability. "Bomber", who earned his nickname from his days as an army explosives expert, replaces long-time Rovers' favourite Hughie Griffiths at right-half.

Griffiths retired in the off-season after many years of loyal service to Rovers. At one stage, Hughie was tipped to take over from Andy McDonald as team captain a few seasons ago, but a bad injury saw him miss most of the season and the captaincy passed, permanently, to Roy Race.

Race himself has not looked back since being named captain and will be striving this season to establish himself as one of the country's leading players and must surely be in the mind of the England selectors.

DECEMBER '62

In the middle of a busy league season, Rovers were involved in a special European challenge match against crack German side Durmstadt. Keen to impress, Rovers played above themselves registering a magnificient 2-1 first leg lead at Melchester Stadium. Both goals were scored by Roy Race, who showed he could step up in class against foreign opposition.

In the second leg, in Germany, Rovers soon found themselves 2-0 down against a more determined German team, but Rovers rallied – again thanks to two goals by Roy Race – to lift the coveted challenge trophy 4-3 on aggregate. Roy Race had arrived on the international stage!

JANUARY '63

FA Cup 3rd Round
Mowbray Town v Melchester Rovers

Rovers were knocked out of the F.A. Cup, by Fourth Division Mowbray Town.

Before the game Rovers knew they would be tested by the famous Mowbray sloping pitch and small, enclosed stadium. But their first half performance must be ranked among their all-time low points. Defenders were in total disarray as they tried to combat wave after wave of Mowbray attacks. How they managed to limit the home side to only four first half goals is beyond belief, as a double-figure scoreline would not have been out of place.

To their credit, Rovers came back strongly in the second half and just failed to send the tie into a less-than deserved replay. Race's second-half hat-trick almost saved the day for Rovers.

Rovers took solace from this defeat in their improved league position, but their concerted championship challenge was in danger of a being over-shadowed by the strong possibility of Roy's inclusion in the England squad.

1962-63

41

THE DELIGHTED ROVERS MOBBED THEIR SKIPPER

YOU WERE RIGHT, BLACKIE! AFTER ALL THAT PRACTICE WITH THE HEADING-MACHINE, I COULD HEAD A FOOTBALL THROUGH A PORT-HOLE!

NOW WE KNOW WHAT TO DO, SKIPPER — KEEP THE BALL IN THE AIR, AND LEAVE THE REST TO YOU!

WITHIN MOMENTS OF THE RESTART, A HIGH CLEARANCE FROM OSSIE JONES WENT SOARING DOWN THE MIDDLE

PHEW! THE BALL'S DROPPING INTO THE PENALTY AREA! IF ONLY ROY CAN GET HIS HEAD TO IT!

NOT A CHANCE! HE'S STANDING WITH HIS BACK TO THE GOAL!

BUT THAT DIDN'T DETER ROY. A MIGHTY, ARCHING LEAP CAUGHT THE EASTOKE GOALIE FLAT-FOOTED!

IT'S THERE — A SMASHING REVERSE HEADER!

HOW DOES HE DO IT?

EVEN THE CLOSEST MARKING BY THE DEFENDERS COULDN'T STOP ROVERS' SKIPPER

GOAL! THAT'S ROY'S HAT-TRICK!

YOU MEAN, 'HEAD-TRICK'! LET'S HAVE ANOTHER, MATE!

JUST TO SHOW THAT HE HAD REALLY 'FOUND HIS FEET', ROY GOT HIS FOURTH WITH A SEARING, 25-YARD DRIVE...!

OH, LOVELY GOAL! THEY JUST CAN'T HOLD HIM!

WHAT A PLAYER!

MELCHESTER ROVERS 4, EASTOKE UNITED 1!

THAT WAS THE SCORE AT FULL-TIME. THREE ENGLAND SELECTORS EXCHANGED GLANCES AS THE TEAMS CAME OFF THE FIELD

WELL...I THINK WE'VE SEEN WHAT WE WANTED

YES... NOW WE MUST REPORT BACK! THE FINAL DECISION RESTS WITH THE FULL SELECTION COMMITTEE

IN THE DRESSING-ROOM, ROY WAS TOO KEYED-UP TO EVEN THINK ABOUT CHANGING

GOSH! I — I WONDER IF I CAUGHT THE SELECTORS' EYES? MAYBE IF I'D SCORED ANOTHER GOAL—!

YOU DID ALL ANYONE COULD ASK OF YOU, ROY! ALL YOU NEED NOW IS SOMEWHERE TO HANG THAT INTERNATIONAL CAP!

BUT ROY WASN'T CONVINCED. AND, AT NOON THE FOLLOWING THURSDAY...

ROY... IT'S JUST BEEN ANNOUNCED — THE ENGLAND TEAM TO PLAY IN THE NEXT INTERNATIONAL!

OH, MY GOSH! READ IT OUT, TOM! I — I CAN'T BEAR TO LOOK!

IN A HUSHED, BREATHLESS SILENCE, TOM DAWSON READ OUT THE NAMES...

...OUTSIDE-RIGHT — MORRIS... INSIDE-RIGHT — FLAVELL ...CENTRE-FORWARD...

...ROY RACE!

APR '63 – WITH THE NEWS THAT HE'D BEEN PICKED TO MAKE HIS ENGLAND DEBUT AGAINST CARAGUA, ROY WENT ON A GOAL-SCORING SPREE – NOTCHING SEVENTEEN GOALS IN HIS NEXT SIX GAMES. AS A RESULT, ROVERS' LEAGUE FORM PROSPERED AND SAW THEM CHALLENGING FOR THE LEAGUE TITLE.

BUT...ROY'S ENGLAND DEBUT WAS ON THE SAME DAY ROVERS PLAYED TITLE CONTENDERS WELLINGBURY. ROY COULD NOT CONCENTRATE ON HIS DEBUT FOR FEAR OF WHAT WAS HAPPENING BACK AT MELCHESTER, AND ESPECIALLY TO TOM DAWSON, WHO HAD BEEN THREATENED WITH A TRANSFER – IF HIS FORM DID NOT IMPROVE...

I LOVE PARIS AFTER FULL-TIME!

SEP '63 – As League Champions, Rovers were drawn for the first time in their history in the prestigious European Cup – against some of the the finest club teams in the world. But first, Rovers had to set about defending their league crown – which they did resolutely, dropping one point in twelve.

OCT '63 – After an unbeaten run of eleven games Rovers were finally undone by Championship challengers Carford City.

Rovers' league form had spluttered with a number of dropped points and missed goals that saw them slip to fourth in the league – eight points behind Carford City. The Rovers' players had one eye firmly set on the upcoming European Cup campaign.

1st Round

1st Leg	Schonved [Hungary] 0	Rovers 0
2nd Leg	Rovers 1	Schonved 0
	Race	(Rovers win 1-0 on agg)

2nd Round

1st Leg	Rovers 0	Kelbridge City [Ire] 1
2nd Leg	Kelbridge City 0	Rovers 2
		Race, Reeves

(Rovers win 2-1 on aggregate)

3rd Round

1st Leg	Rovers 1	Doledo [Hungary] 1
	Race	*[Defending champions]*
2nd Leg	Doledo 1	Rovers 2
		Gray, Race

(Rovers win 3-2 on aggregate)

Semi-final

1st Leg	Stalzburg [W. Ger] 1	Rovers 0
2nd Leg	Rovers 3	Stalzburg 0
	Gray, Race (2)	

(Rovers win 3-1 on aggregate)

MAY '64 – Rovers' league title had been taken by Carford City, while the F.A. Cup had seen yet another early departure (two-one to local rivals Cranville United in the Fourth Round).

JUN '64 – Before the European Cup Final in Paris, against Italian side Nettruno, Blackie Gray having got himself mixed up with a French movie actress Suzanne Cerise and stuntman Ed Garrard was late for the game...

MELCHESTER ROVERS 0   NETTRUNO 1

1963-64

Roy OF THE Rovers

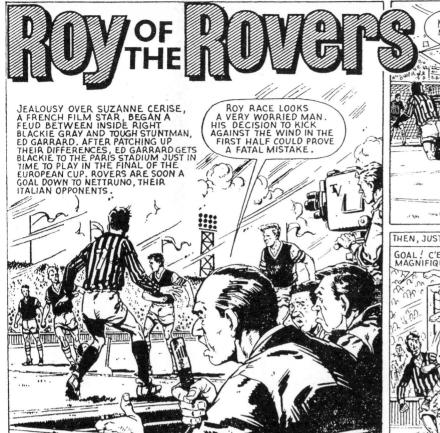

1963-64

MAY THE JUICE BE WITH YOU!

AUGUST '64

ROVERS MISSING! PRESUMED KIDNAPPED!

The whole of the Melchester Rovers football team has been reported missing while on a brief tour of South America. The team flew out two days ago to the republic of Malagos to play a World Club Cup game against local side Bagota.

After arriving in Malagos City to a full presidential welcome the team were last seen at their training ground in the nearby hills.

No report has yet been received from any member of the team as to their whereabouts, which has caused great confusion in the sleepy republic.

Not only must the team's disappearance throw doubt on their participation in the World Club Cup game against Bagota in three days time, but seriously threatens their chances of fulfilling their domestic commitments when the league season kicks off next week.

The British Consulate in Malagos City is holding an emergency meeting with the president to locate the missing players...

AUGUST '64

Rovers had been kidnapped, by local brigands, not for political purposes, but for sporting reasons. It seems Rovers' reputation had managed to permeate the dense jungle of South America. Forced to march through rain-forest, Rovers were made to take part in a match between two rival bands of rebels.

After reluctantly agreeing to play, Rovers proceeded to put on an exhibition of football for their "hosts". The final score-line, 17-2, showed Rovers' undoubted superiority, but at a cost. The rough-house tactics of their opponents left every Rovers' player nursing bumps and bruises. Despite their ordeal, the players managed to escape on horse-back and arrived in Malagos City only minutes before the kick-off – having not had any sleep for 48 hours...

1964-65

47

ROVERS DIDN'T HAVE TO GO LOOKING FOR THEIR FORMER CAPTORS, BRUNO AND BEPPO, WHO WERE WAITING FOR THEM IN THEIR DRESSING ROOM AT HALF-TIME. THE BRIGAND LEADERS ASSURED THE PLAYERS THAT THEIR INTENTIONS WERE NOW STRICTLY HONOURABLE. AS THANKS FOR WINNING THE "REBEL" GAME, BRUNO AND BEPPO GAVE THE TEAM A REJUVENATING POTION CALLED "CARIOCA JUICE". THE TIRED TEAM DRANK THEIR FILL AND A TRANSFORMATION CAME OVER THEM. MINUTES LATER, A NEW TEAM WERE READY FOR THE SECOND HALF.

SEPTEMBER '64

ROVERS LORD IT OVER SANDFORD

Melchester Rovers 4   Sandford Athletic 2

Against much-fancied Sandford, Rovers showed their experience in playing the best teams in the world has translated into top form in their domestic fixtures. Down two early goals, Rovers stormed back to win an almighty encounter with four of their own well-taken strikes.

Key to Rovers' continuing confidence and success is new signing, at inside-left, Lord D'arcy Plantagenet Trudgeon-Marclay. Better known in the circles of royalty and society as, Lord 'Jumbo' Trudgeon, he has agreed to join Rovers on a no-pay, no-contract deal. A multi-millionaire landowner, Trudgeon has no need of seeking a living from football. He has quickly proved that he will not be a fish out of water – his second-half hat-trick against Sandford bodes of many great things for his future.

OCT '64 – UNFORTUNATELY, JUMBO'S RICH SENSE OF ENTER-
PRISE LEAD TO THE TEAM IGNORING THEIR FOOTBALLING
DUTIES TO SEEK OUT NEW ADVENTURES, AND GO WHERE NO
FOOTBALL TEAM HAS EVER GONE BEFORE. THE TEAM'S
INTRODUCTION TO THE JET-SETTING HIGH LIFE ALMOST COST
ROVERS DEAR ON THE PITCH....

AFTER MILFORD PULLED A GOAL BACK, JUMBO SET UP BLACKIE GRAY FOR ROVERS' THIRD.
FINAL SCORE – MILFORD 1   ROVERS 3

NOV '64 – LEAGUE TABLE – TOP FOUR							
	P	W	D	L	F	A	Pts
Melchester Rovers	16	10	4	2	34	8	24
Milford United	16	9	4	3	28	13	22
Kingsbay	15	7	6	2	27	15	20
Portdean City	16	8	2	6	24	18	18

MELCHESTER ROVERS, FIGHTING FOR THE LEAGUE CHAMPIONSHIP, WERE AT LAST BACK ON THEIR HOME GROUND, FORMERLY DAMAGED BY FLOOD WATER. ANY BAD LUCK OVERSHADOWING THEM SEEMED TO BE LIFTING, AS ROY SCORED IN THE FIRST HALF OF THEIR MATCH AGAINST SILFORD ATHLETIC. LORD JUMBO TRUDGEON, ROVERS' MULTI-MILLIONAIRE INSIDE LEFT, WAS ALSO IN CRACKING FORM...

BACK TO NORMAL! MORE LIKE OLD TIMES, ROY. WE JUST KEEP OUR 'SHOOTING BOOTS' ON AND PLAY SILFORD INTO THE GROUND.

SHUT UP, YOU'RE CROWDING OUR LUCK, BLACKIE. MAKES ME WONDER WHAT CAN GO WRONG.

JUMBO'S CHANCE CAME NEXT...

HIT IT, LOOOORDY! COME ON! HE CAN'T LOSE UNLESS THE GROUND SWALLOWS HIM!

SUDDENLY THE PITCH SEEMED TO SAG...

'PON MY WORD, THE PITCH IS BREAKING UP!

WHAT ON EARTH...?

HA, HA, HA... GOING DOWN, ROVERS!

HE--HE'S SINKING. THE EARTH HAS SWALLOWED HIM!

THE MATCH WAS ABANDONED.

A PITCH SUBSIDENCE---ISN'T IT MARVELLOUS---EVERYTHING HAPPENS TO ROVERS. TALK ABOUT LUCK!

I RECKON WE PLAYED YOU INTO THE GROUND, ROVERS!

MAY '65

Like their pitch, Melchester Rovers' season also crumbled about their boot-straps.

Forced to play away from the inspiring surroundings of Melchester Stadium, Rovers' promising early season league form subsided badly and the team just held on to finish a bitterly disappointing sixth by the seasons' close.

But, the F.A. Cup was proving to be a different matter...

Jan '65 – 3rd Round
Linfield 0 Rovers 3
Race (2), Gray

Feb '65 – 4th Round
Rovers 5 Grove Athletic 1
Race (3), Trudgeon (2)

Mar '65 – 5th Round
Rovers 4 Brookleigh Wdrs 0
Mann (2), Race (2)

Apr '65 – 6th Round
Cranville United 2 Rovers 2
Mann (2)

Replay
Rovers 2 Cranville United 1
Carter, Dawson

Apr '65 – Semi-Final
Rovers 3 Meltham Rangers 4
Trudgeon, Race, Gray

GOALKEEPER TURNED GOAL-POACHER!

NOVEMBER '65

EURO CUP SHOCKER!

ROVERS HAMMERED BY NORWEGIAN PART-TIMERS!

Trondheim 1   Melchester Rovers 0 (Agg 1-0)

JANUARY '66

LEAGUE CUP SHOCKER!

Melchester Rovers 1   Midbury Town 2

...Despite going out of of their second cup competition in the early rounds, captain Roy Race refuses to write-off the whole season, "There's still another trophy to be won! With luck this might be our year in the F.A. Cup! But it's going to be a long hard road to Wembley! But we won't cross our bridges before we've counted them." Rovers having beaten Second Division Kenton United 2-1 in the Third round of the F.A. Cup meet Fourth Division giant-killers Flaxton Town in the next round.

FEBRUARY '66

ROVERS SCRAPE A REPLAY WITH GIANT-KILLERS

ROVERS HUMILIATED BY FLAXTON TOWN

FA Cup, Fourth round
Melchester Rovers 1   Flaxton Town 1

A last-second Roy Race thunderbolt saved Rovers' blushes against this season's Cup giant-killers.The Fourth Division side are going to be more than a match for Rovers on their own sloping pitch in Wednesday's replay. Roy Race will need all his experience for Rovers to reach the Fifth round.

FEBRUARY '66

TUBBY FLATTENS FLAXTON

FA Cup, Fourth round replay
Flaxton Town 0   Melchester Rovers 1

...In extra-time, after a goal-less ninety minutes, Rovers' Dawson was injured and was unable to continue. Changing places with goalkeeper Morton, Dawson somehow thwarted Flaxton's attacks. With both teams exhausted, after almost three and a half hours of all out commitment, one man stepped up to settle this enthralling cup-tie. Morton picked up a through ball from Roy Race, took the ball in his stride and lobbed the 'keeper for the only goal.

Other F.A. Cup Results:

5th Round
Melchester Rovers 2   Portdean City 1
Race (2 – 1 pen)

6th Round
Melchester Rovers 1   Shermall Athletic 1
Race

Replay
Shermall Athletic 1   Melchester Rovers 2
Race, Gray

Semi-final
Melchester Rovers 2   Kelford City 1
Jones, Race

Final
Melchester Rovers v Eastoke United
(League Champions)

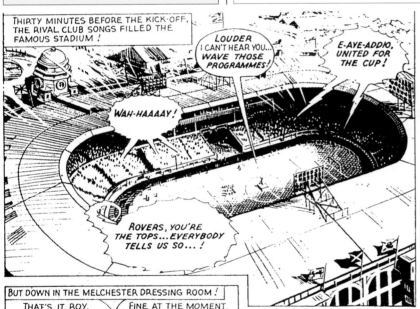

BOTH TEAMS STARTED THE GAME AT A CRACKING PACE . . .

1965-66

ROVERS' TEAM SHEET

1 TUBBY MORTON
2 DAVE WILLIAMS
3 BOB ROBERTS
4 BOMBER REEVES
5 OSSIE JONES
6 HUGH GRIFFITHS

7 TONY STORME
8 BLACKIE GRAY
9 ROY RACE
10 JUMBO TRUDGEON
11 TOM DAWSON

1965-66

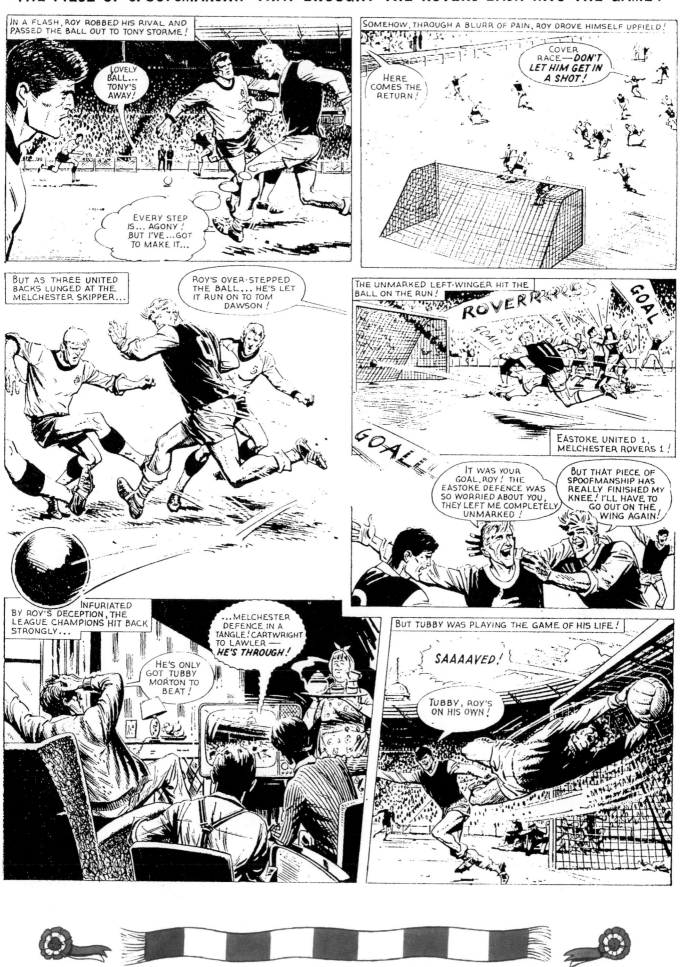

GLORIOUS GOAL IN THE DYING SECONDS OF THE MATCH!

1965-66

IN TUNE ROVERS ON SONG FOR EUROPE

AUGUST '66

A horrific motorcycle accident ended the playing careers of veteran Melchester defenders Dave Williams and Bob Roberts. The pair, who had last played for Rovers in the FA Cup final, suffered multiple fractures in a high speed collision during a Charity speedway soccer event.

Without these experienced defenders Rovers' early league form didn't look good, lying a mediocre twelfth place in the league by October. Young reserve team defenders Ken Cooper and Derek Millar were moved into the first team and slowly they began to provide Rovers with a credible defence. With league ambitions in abeyance, Rovers set their sights on the European Cup-Winners' Cup.

OCTOBER '66

European Cup-Winners' Cup
Preliminary Round, 2nd leg
Melchester Rovers v Villa Florina [Italy]

A dejected Rovers had returned home from the first Leg of their tie with Villa Florina one goal down. In the second leg, Rovers were taken aback by Florina's unexpected attacking approach and conceded a goal in the very first minute. At half-time, they were staring elimination in the face needing three goals to win.

But as the minutes ticked away late in the second half, the Italians ran out of puff. Rovers displaying superior fitness pounced in numbers, scoring three quick goals courtesy of Roy Race, Jumbo Trudgeon and Blackie Gray. With a three-two aggregate win Melchester had at last steam-rollered over an exhausted Florino.

NOVEMBER '66

European Cup-Winners' Cup
First Round, 2nd leg
Melchester Rovers v Paniakos [Greece]

Rovers had come back from their first leg away to the Greek cup-holders with a comfortable two goals to one lead. Replacement inside-left Thumper Thorpe was the man to thank for both goals.

But Rovers' regular number ten Jumbo Trudgeon, had declared himself fit for the second leg, so it was hard cheese for Thumper Thorpe who had played a vital role in Rovers' away win.

At Melchester, the Greeks sprang a surprise of Trojan proportions. They scored early on and, with away goals counting double, held onto a winning position until the last move of the game, Rovers mounted a final onslaught...

FROM A CORNER TO ROVERS, RACE UNLEASHED A VOLLEY, ONLY TO HIT THE POST! A HUGE SIGH ROSE FROM THE CROWD WHO THOUGHT IT WAS ALL OVER...

ROVERS WIN 3-2 ON AGGREGATE

DECEMBER '66

European Cup-Winners' Cup
Second Round, 1st leg
Karspor [Turkey] v Melchester Rovers

Rovers, wallowing in the bottom half of the league table, failed to score in a goalless first half of their tough away leg against the slick Turkish cup-holders. In the second-half, the setting sun blazed down on the Rovers' goal with dazzling intensity. Blinded, goalkeeper Tubby Morton had little chance against Karspor's relentless attacks on his goal and did well to restrict the Turkish side to a two goal lead at full-time. Rovers faced an uphill task to stay in the cup.

JANUARY '67

European Cup-Winners' Cup
Second Round, 2nd leg
Melchester Rovers v Karspor [Turkey]

...As they took to the pitch for the second half Rovers needed to score three goals or say goodbye to their cup aspirations. Rising to the challenge left winger Tony Storme led a dramatic rearguard action with two quick goals. With seconds to go before full-time and Karspor poised to win on the away goals rule, Roy Race, injured in a previous tackle, courageously ploughed on and managed to execute an inch-perfect cross to Storme and...

ROVERS WIN 3-2 ON AGGREGATE

MARCH '67

ROVERS REIGN IN SPAIN

European Cup-Winners' Cup semi-final
Melchester Rovers v Real Corbao [Spain]

Melchester Rovers may not have performed well at home to Spain's Real Corbao, losing two-one in the first leg. But in Spain, Rovers turned on the style which has pulled them through from the brink of defeat in Europe so often this season.

Once more Rovers waited until the second-half to shift their mighty machine into top gear. Captain Roy Race orchestrated a brilliant new tactic to break the deadlock, putting Corbao's left-back, Hernandez, under extraordinarily intense pressure. Twice, the easily flustered defender failed to clear the ball effectively and twice Roy Race pounced and rocketed the ball in the "lobster pot". Astute tactics, backed by precision finishing put Rovers, ironically facing relegation in the league, through to the Final of the European Cup-Winners' Cup.

ROY'S FIRST IN ROVERS' SEMI-FINAL WIN OVER REAL CORBAO.

1967 EUROPEAN CUP-WINNERS' CUP FINAL
MELCHESTER ROVERS v SPORTING ALCERO [PORTUGAL]

HAMPDEN PARK, SCOTLAND

ROY REALISED THAT ALCERO'S TOWERING CENTRE-FORWARD COULD BE THE FOCUS OF AN AERIAL ASSAULT ON THE ROVERS' GOAL. EARLY ON ALCERO EARNED A CORNER AND PROVED JUST HOW RIGHT HE WAS....

ROY ESCAPED, THANKS TO THE QUICK-WITTED ACTIONS OF A MEMBER OF THE CROWD WHO HAD CAUGHT THE BANNER IN THE NICK OF TIME. YOUNG 'JOCK,' ONE OF A GROUP OF JUNIOR FOOTBALL CLUB PLAYERS, ROVERS HAD INVITED ALONG TO THE FINAL HAD BECOME AN INSTANT FAN OF ROVERS.

THE GAME'S WON AND ROVERS ARE EUROPEAN CHAMPIONS!

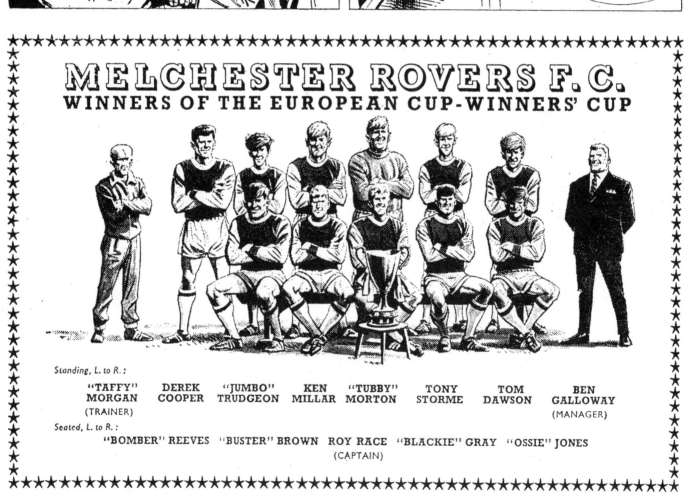

MELCHESTER ROVERS F.C.
WINNERS OF THE EUROPEAN CUP-WINNERS' CUP

Standing, L. to R. :

"TAFFY" MORGAN (TRAINER) DEREK COOPER "JUMBO" TRUDGEON KEN MILLAR "TUBBY" MORTON TONY STORME TOM DAWSON BEN GALLOWAY (MANAGER)

Seated, L. to R. :

"BOMBER" REEVES "BUSTER" BROWN ROY RACE (CAPTAIN) "BLACKIE" GRAY "OSSIE" JONES

1966-67

MAY '67

Rovers had managed to gain their European Cup-Winners' Cup success at the expense of a poor domestic league campaign.

The last few months of the season had seen a succession of disappointing results as Rovers struggled with ever-increasing problems concerning fitness and morale.

Nearing the end of the season as Rovers were inevitably sucked into the relegation zone, it looked as if the unthinkable might happen, that Rovers would go down.

In March, Rovers' late season form did not show any sign of improvement as they continued to drop points at an alarming rate.

Melchester Rovers 0   Portdean 0

Tynecaster 3   Melchester Rovers 1
Race

Melboro 4   Melchester Rovers 3
Trudgeon (3)

In April, bad luck struck Rovers when three of their star players, Trudgeon, Cooper and

Millar arrived late and missed a vital away game against Toncaster, when Jumbo Trudgeon's chauffeur-driven Bentley broke down on the way to the stadium. Without the missing trio, a hastily reshuffled Rovers' side were no match for the 'Tons'.

Melchester Rovers 0   Toncaster 1

Melchester Rovers 1   Bradport United 0
Race

Rovers' narrow win over Bradport United, thanks to a net-busting blast from skipper Race, had broken their drought of victories. But they remained deep in trouble at the foot of the division, staring Division Two

squarely in the face. They needed to win their last home match, against Melboro, 4-0 to avoid relegation.

A promised tour of the United States of America also depended on Rovers remainng in the top flight. If that wasn't enough, their opponents, Melboro, were fierce local rivals, who would like nothing more than to be the club to send Rovers to their embarrassing doom. On the eve of the game, the whole of Melchester had become very tense, as the city, divided by fervent support, prepared iteself for its biggest local derby for many years.

But as game the kicked off, Rovers swept all the pressures aside and took the game to Melboro with unstoppable gusto...

DIVISION ONE LEAGUE TABLE – BOTTOM FOUR

	P	W	D	L	F	A	Pts
Eastgate	42	10	12	20	46	78	32
North Vale	42	7	14	21	43	81	28
Melchester	41	7	12	21	40	81	26
Gatesfield	42	4	9	28	23	96	17

1966-67

61

GOAL-SCORING RECORDS, LIKE PROMISES, WERE MADE TO BE BROKEN

FEBRUARY '68

MELCHESTER WIN ROVERS CLASH

Rochington Rovers 1   Melchester Rovers 3

Rovers increase their slender lead at the top despite giving away an early goal, and then having two goals disallowed.

First, full-back Derek Cooper played an ill-judged pass across his goal which was pounced on by Rochington's Ray Wellington to give the visitors a shock lead.

After Roy Race's shot was handled on the line, Cooper's spot-kick came back off the bar and was calmly knocked in by the full-back. Referee Mr White disallowed the goal, since no other player had touched the ball after Cooper's penalty kick.

In the second half, Terry West lobbed the stranded goalkeeper, but a linesman flagged him offside. After these set-backs, Rovers hit a purple patch of perfection, as Roy Race, following in a Trudgeon shot, nodded home the first – despite appeals for another offside.

Rovers added two more, from Gray – after a goalmouth scramble – and the irrepressible Trudgeon – with an unstoppable cannonball from twenty yards.

MARCH '68

ROY RACE'S CHANCE TO MAKE MELCHESTER HISTORY!

AS ROVERS' PREPARED THEMSELVES FOR THEIR NEXT GAME AGAINST SEAFORD, THERE WAS A SENSE OF HISTORY IN THE MAKING....

TWO QUICK GOALS SENT THE FANS WILD WITH DELIGHT !

ROY of the ROVERS

IN THE DYING SECONDS OF THE SEAFORD GAME, ROY RACE BROKE THE ROVERS' THIRTY YEAR SCORING RECORD WITH HIS 300TH GOAL.

IN THE FINAL LEAGUE MATCH OF THE SEASON, MELCHESTER ROVERS WERE PLAYING HIGHWOOD ATHLETIC, WHO WERE TOP OF THE TABLE WITH 58 POINTS. MELCHESTER WERE SECOND WITH 57. VICTORY WOULD GIVE ROVERS THE CHAMPIONSHIP. BUT HIGHWOOD ONLY HAD TO DRAW TO TAKE THE TITLE THEMSELVES. WITHIN A FEW MINUTES OF THE START, ROVERS SKIPPER ROY RACE WAS INJURED AND CARRIED OFF. BUT, TO THE AMAZEMENT OF THE FANS, MANAGER BEN GALLOWAY REFUSED TO ALLOW THE SUBSTITUTE, ALEC BLACKBURN, TO TAKE ROY'S PLACE. ALEC WAS DISGUSTED...

I'VE WAITED WEEKS FOR A CHANCE. NOW THAT IT'S COME, YOU WON'T LET ME TAKE IT.

BEN, I THINK IT'LL BE BEST IF ALEC GOES ON.

NO!

BEN, WE'VE ALWAYS BEEN AGREED. AS MANAGER YOU RUN THE CLUB, BUT AS SKIPPER, I RUN THE TEAM.

BUT YOU AREN'T SKIPPER WHILE YOU'RE LYING THERE, BLACKIE IS — AND HE'LL BE GUIDED BY ME.

LOOK, TAFFY MAY BE ABLE TO GET YOU FIT! ONCE THE SUBSTITUTE'S ON, I CAN'T TAKE HIM OFF AND SEND YOU BACK ON... OR HAD YOU FORGOTTEN THAT?

HIGHWOOD WERE MAKING THE MOST OF THEIR ONE-MAN ADVANTAGE.

GET THE BALL AWAY, ROVERS. MAKE A BREAK!

THEY DON'T REALISE THAT HIGHWOOD HAVE GOT A SPARE MAN ON THE LOOSE ALL THE TIME.

LOOK! ROY'S ON HIS FEET!

HOW DOES IT FEEL, ROY?

OKAY! TAFFY'S A GENIUS! GUESS YOU MADE THE RIGHT DECISION, BEN. I'M FIT TO GO BACK.

1967-68

A PACKED DEFENCE HELD THE MIGHTY MELCHESTER ATTACK!

BLACKIE GRAY

Melchester Rovers and England Inside Right

Roy Race reminisces about his great pal and striking partner Blackie Gray.

"Perhaps you have wondered whether Blackie has a proper first name? I'll tell you right away that he has – William, named after his eccentric great-grand-uncle. William has been known, as long as I have known him, as Blackie, because of the shock of dense jet-black hair that surmounts a clever mind. I first met Blackie at Melchester Grammar school, where he was the inspirational captain of the football team. I found out straight away that Blackie was a decent sort of chap, who could be trusted as a pal. And pals we became, and pals we have stayed for all these years. At school we had our share of matey scrapes and japes, which have seemed to follow us through our adult career.

Once we had played our first game together our footballing lives have been forever entwined. We both progressed through the school teams, we won local representative honours together, we both joined Melchester Rovers as apprentices together and then worked our way through the Rovers' team system until we made out first team debut together in 1955.

Over the years Blackie and I, and our families, have become very close and many people think we must be brothers. However much time we spend with each other, there is nothing that we like doing better than scoring goals together!"

REBEL WITHOUT A CONTRACT CLAUSE!

AUGUST '68

ROVERS SIGN BALLARD FOR RECORD £150,000

Ben Galloway, yesterday purchased the missing link to his club's challenge for the European Cup. Carford United's centre-half Douglas Ballard, is seen as the replacement for Ossie Jones who recently took the manager's job at Highwood.

Ballard, whose past record is not inspiring, four clubs in four years, has the reputation of a rebel and trouble-maker. He will need to mend his ways quickly, with the first round of the European Cup – against Shevnik Sparta – in three weeks. Galloway sees Ballard settling in at Rovers very quickly, "What Ballard needs is the right team spirit – he will be a player at Melchester for many years to come."

OCTOBER '68

BEN BLACKBALLS BALLARD !

After a series of temperamental outbursts, Douglas Ballard, Rover's recent record signing, has been sacked by manager Ben Galloway. Galloway blames Ballard for the club's recent defeat at home in the European Cup by Shevnik Sparta. After only two games, and having replaced Roy Race as club captain, it seems Ballard quickly managed to wear out his welcome at Rovers. Galloway will be looking to replace Ballard at the first opportunity.

European Cup

NOV '68 – 1st Round, 2nd Leg
Shevnik Sparta [Hungary] 2   Rovers 3
(On aggregate 4-4, Rovers win on away goals rule)

As cover for "Bomber" Reeves, who broke his leg after falling out of the airplane on the team's victorious return to Melchester after defeating Shevnik Sparta, Ben Galloway has signed youngster Geoff Giles.

DEC '68 – As replacement for "Buster" Brown who recently retired from playing, Ben Galloway has signed Kingsbay's "Gentle Giant" Lofty Peak.

Brown will team up with "Bomber" Reeves who also hung his boots up after recently breaking his leg. Both former players have set up Melchester Rovers' first Souvenir Shop just around the corner from Melchester Stadium. Left-half Brown has been with Rovers since 1956, while Reeves – "The Hardest Head In Football" – made his Rovers' debut in 1962.

Both will be missed from the field of play, but don't forget to pop in to their new shop.

JAN '69 – 2nd Round
1st Leg   Vardennes [France] 2   Rovers 0
2nd Leg   Rovers 3   Vardennes 0 (aet)
(Rovers win 3-2 on agg.)

MAR '69 – 3rd Round
1st Leg   Limosia [Cyprus] 0   Rovers 0
2nd Leg   Rovers 3   Limosia 2
(Rovers win 3-2 on agg.)

APR '69 – Semi-Final
1st Leg   Leonardo [Italy] 1   Rovers 1
2nd Leg   Rovers 0   Leonardo 0
(On agg. 1-1, Rovers win on away goals)

MAY '69 – Just before the European Cup Final, in Paris against Portuguese champions Santova Rapid, Blackie Gray was kicked in the head by a horse and suffered a bad concussion. Passed fit to play, by trainer Taffy Morgan, Roy Race was not so sure of his team-mate's state of mind...

ROY KEPT A WATCHFUL EYE ON BLACKIE. AS THE ROVERS PREPARED FOR THE KICK-OFF.

BLACKIE, ARE YOU SURE YOU'RE ALL RIGHT?

STOP FUSSING! THIS IS SUCH A BIG MATCH FOR ROVERS I WOULDN'T TAKE CHANCES. I'M NOT THAT SELFISH.

SANTOVA RAPID STARTED THE GAME AS IF THEY MEANT TO RUN ROVERS OFF THEIR FEET. GOALIE TUBBY MORTON WAS QUICKLY BROUGHT INTO ACTION.

WELL SAVED, TUBBY!

LOFTY PEAK PICKED UP TUBBY'S LONG CLEARANCE AND SLANTED IT ACROSS TO BLACKIE.

BLACKIE'S IN GREAT FORM — THANK GOODNESS.

WITH TIME RUNNING OUT, TUBBY MORTON SENT A LONG BALL FORWARD....

ALTHOUGH BLACKIE WAS NOT WELL ENOUGH TO JOIN HIS TRIUMPHANT TEAM-MATES IN A LAP OF HONOUR,
HE WAS ABLE TO JOIN THEM FOR THEIR UPCOMING TOUR OF MEXICO.

JACKPOT VERNON'S SPOT-THE-BALL WIZARD

AUGUST '69

After returning from Mexico, where they had shared the invitational tournament with South American club champions Sao Madro Nacional, Rovers prepared for a new league season...

Melchester Rovers 1   Stanport 1
Race (pen)
Portdean City 2   Melchester Rovers 0
Melchester Rovers 0   Shenton United 1
Weston Athletic 2   Melchester Rovers 1
Gray

SEPTEMBER '69

ROVERS STOP ROT!

With just one point from their first four league games, Rovers finally notched their first win of the season - over Eastoke United. New signing, winger Vernon Eliot, set Rovers on their way with a goal on his debut, while a late Race "special delivery" saw Rovers pick up the two points. This timely win puts Rovers in a better frame of mind for their forthcoming World Club Cup Final against Sao Madro Nacional.

SEPTEMBER '69

Thanks to two goals from skipper Roy Race, Rovers drew the away leg of the World Club Cup Final against Sao Madro.

In the first half, of the second leg, against Nacional, Rovers' full-back Ken Cooper was badly injured and replaced by young Chalky White.

White's inexperience under pressure saw him concede a penalty which Nacional duly converted. This cancelled out Blackie Gray's left foot strike after only thirty seconds.

Boosted by their World Club Cup victory, Rovers' form improved dramatically over their next few domestic games....

Melchester Rovers 3   Cranville Athletic 0
Race, Eliot, Trudgeon

Lintown 0   Melchester Rovers 4
Dylan, Race, Eliot, White

Melchester Rovers 4   Weston Athletic 0
Eliot, Race, Gray, Trudgeon

By Christmas, Rovers were second in the league to Portdean City. But the New Year saw Rovers embark on another rousing F.A. Cup campaign....

3rd Round
Melchester Rovers 1   Molton United 1
Race [Giles sent off]
Replay
Molton United 1   Melchester Rovers 2
                              West, Race
4th Round
Woodburn Spartan 1   Melchester Rovers 1
[Non-league]   *Eager*
Replay
Melchester Rovers 7   Woodburn Spartan 0
Race (3), West, Trudgeon, Peak, Gray
5th Round
Melchester Rovers 1   Corstone City 0
Race
6th Round
Kingsbay 0   Melchester Rovers 1
                              West

Semi-final
Millborough 1   Melchester Rovers 2
                              Race, Eliot

MAY '70 – By the time Rovers had reached another Wembley Cup Final, they had lost their way in the league, finishing fourth. Although, three of their players – Race, Morton and Giles – had been selected for England's World Cup Squad for Mexico.

In the Final, against Seaford Athletic, a bad clearance ricocheting in off an attacker, by England keeper Tubby Morton, gave Seaford an early lead aginst the run of play.

With Seaford defending their goal under a second-half onslaught, Vernon Eliot's injury time, pinpoint volley from an acute angle sent the Final into extra-time.

ROY RACE WAS SKIPPER OF FIRST DIVISION MELCHESTER ROVERS. THEY WERE PLAYING SEAFORD ATHLETIC IN THE F.A. CUP FINAL AT WEMBLEY AND AT THE END OF THE SECOND HALF THE SCORE WAS 1-1. IT MEANT THAT THEY WERE GOING TO HAVE TO PLAY HALF AN HOUR OF EXTRA TIME, AND SOME OF THE PLAYERS WERE COMPLAINING TO MANAGER BEN GALLOWAY THAT THEY WOULDN'T BE ABLE TO LAST OUT.

I PACED MYSELF TO LAST NINETY MINUTES. I NEVER BARGAINED FOR THIS. I'M CREASED.

ME TOO! I CAN HARDLY PUT ONE FOOT IN FRONT OF THE OTHER.

ALL OF YOU, LISTEN TO ME...

THE F.A. CUP ISN'T WON BY SOFTIES. SEAFORD HAVE HAD AN EXHAUSTING TIME, TOO. I PRIDE MYSELF ON PRODUCING THE FITTEST PLAYERS IN THE GAME.

SEAFORD STARTED OFF AT A TREMENDOUS PACE...

SEAFORD ARE CHUCKING EVERYTHING IN FOR ANOTHER QUICK GOAL.

PHEW! THEY'LL NEVER KEEP THIS UP.

ROVERS' GOALIE TUBBY MORTON DEALT GALLANTLY WITH EVERYTHING SEAFORD COULD SLAM AT HIM.

GOOD OLD TUBBY. KEEP 'EM OUT.

AT THE END OF THE FIRST FIFTEEN MINUTES THERE HAD STILL BEEN NO FURTHER SCORE.

THEY MUST BE ABSOLUTELY EXHAUSTED.

IF ROVERS ARE GOING TO WIN THIS THEY'LL HAVE TO GET A MOVE ON. THEY'VE ONLY GOT ANOTHER QUARTER OF AN HOUR.

ROY SIGNALLED TO THE ROVERS THAT NOW WAS THE MOMENT TO GO FLAT OUT...

A FEW MINUTES LATER ROY SAW A TELL-TALE SIGN THAT SEAFORD HAD REACHED THE END OF THEIR TETHER.

THEY'RE ROLLING DOWN THEIR STOCKINGS. THEIR LEGS ARE GIVING OUT. NOW'S THE TIME TO HIT 'EM.

BLACKIE GRAY DOESN'T LOOK TIRED ANY MORE!

Continued on next page

THERE'S ALWAYS A RUMOUR AT THE TOP!

EUROPEAN CUP-WINNERS' CUP

OCT '70 – First Round, 1st Leg
Rovers 0   Rythoven Olympic [Greece] 2

First Round, 2nd Leg
Rythoven Olympic 1   Rovers 4
            Race (3), Trudgeon
[Rovers win 4-3 on aggregate]

NOV '70 – Second Round, 1st Leg
Racing Lombardo [Italy] 2   Rovers 0
Second Round, 2nd Leg
Rovers 3   Racing Lombardo 0
Race (3)
[Rovers win 3-2 on aggregate]

JAN '71 – Third Round, 1st Leg
Hagenburg [W.Ger.] 4   Rovers 3
            West, Gray, Race

FEB '71 – Third Round, 2nd Leg
Rovers 4   Hagenburg 3
Roy (3), Eliot
[7-7 on aggregate (after extra time) Rovers

won 3-2 on penalties from Race, Gray and
Morton – who also saved three spot-kicks.]

MAR '71 – Semi-final , 1st Leg
Argarvo Rapido [Portugal] 2   Rovers 2
Trudgeon, Race

APR '71 – Semi-final, 2nd Leg
Melchester Rovers 2   Argarvo Rapido 1
Eliot, Race
[Rovers win 4-3 on aggregate]

**MAY '71 – European Cup Winners'
Cup Final** at Menkdorf Stadium
Rovers v Standard Wasserdram [Belgium]

HURER LOST HIS MARKER

76   1970-71

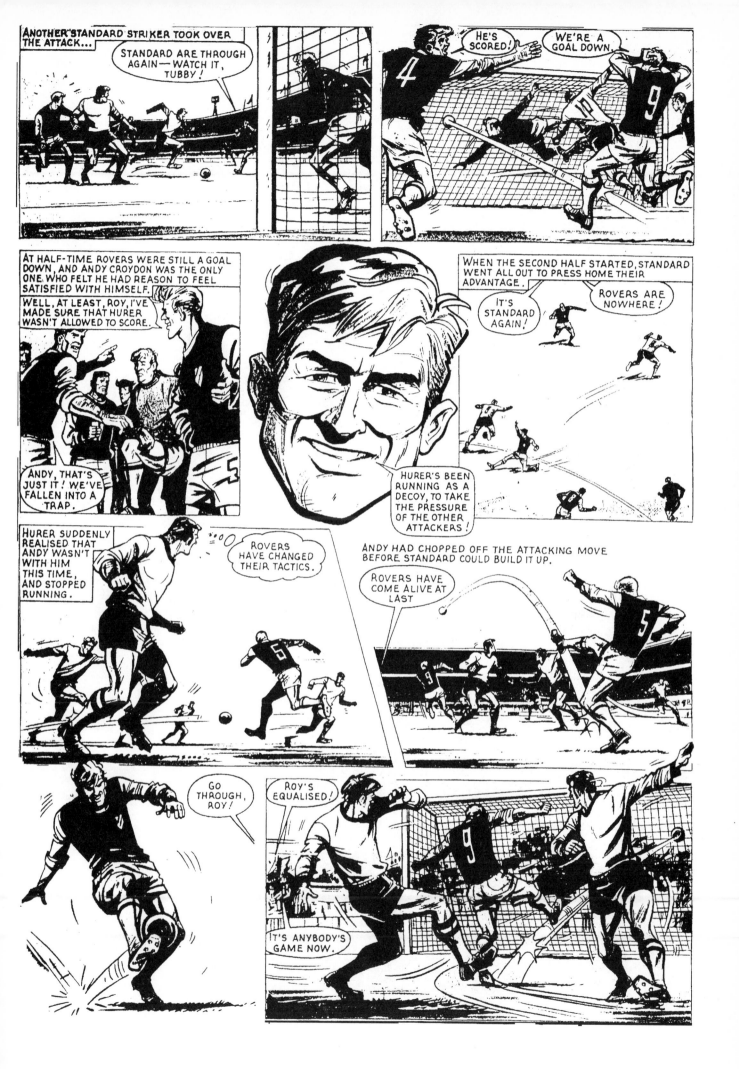

ROY RACE WAS SKIPPER OF FIRST DIVISION MELCHESTER ROVERS, WHO HAD WON THE EUROPEAN CUP-WINNERS' CUP. THE TEAM WERE TAKEN ON A TRIUMPHANT DRIVE THROUGH CHEERING CROWDS TO A CIVIC RECEPTION AT MELCHESTER TOWN HALL...

ROY of the ROVERS

MAY '71 – ROVERS' SUCCESS IN THE EUROPEAN CUP WINNERS' CUP HAD MADE UP FOR A VERY DISAPPOINTING DOMESTIC SEASON. BACK IN JANUARY, KNOCKED OUT OF THE F.A. CUP IN THE THIRD ROUND BY KINGSBAY, WHEN ROVERS WERE WITHOUT CAPTAIN ROY RACE. THAT WEEK'S HEADLINES REVEALED A SENSATIONAL SHOCK...

JAN '71

ROY AND ROVERS TO PART?

KINGSBAY IN SECRET DEAL OVER MELCHESTER CAPTAIN

Reports have been received from Kingsbay that Melchester captain, Roy Race, who was dropped from his side's defeat in the F.A. Cup, has been seen in the town under secretive circumstances. Having booked into Kingsbay's Wilton Hotel, under an assumed name, Race's movements have been mysterious.

What is public knowledge is Kingsbay's desire to sign a top striker to concentrate their efforts on winning Championships with Rovers, and would seem the ideal man to fill Kingsbay's requirements. BUT, will Rovers be persuaded to part with their inspirational leader? And, if so, at what price?

JUNE '71 – The shock story was scotched as a rumour, Roy had been visiting Kingsbay (in secret) to avoid any publicity over his new house purchase, which fell through anyway.

In touch with the leading group throughout much of the season, the Cup-Winners' Cup took much of the team's attention away from the League and they finished a disappointing seventh – some fifteen points below eventual champions Kingsbay.

Roy's thirteen goals in this season's Cup Winners' Cup run was a record for any British player in all three European Cup competitions. Roy also finished top-scorer in England with 48 goals in total – the fifth straight year he had been the country's top marksman..

PAVED WITH GOAL INTENTIONS!

MAY '72 – With the season reaching a climax, Rovers found themselves once again in the F.A. Cup Final at Wembley Stadium –

F.A. Cup Results –
THE ROAD TO WEMBLEY
3rd Round
Melchester Rovers 2   Burnswell [4th Div] 1
Trudgeon, Giles
4th Round
Ashbrook [2nd Div] 2   Melchester Rovers 3
Giles, Race (2)

5th Round
Shenton United 0   Melchester Rovers 2
Race, Gray
6th Round
Melchester Rovers 2   Eastoke United 0
Gray, Race
Semi-final
Melchester Rovers 1   Lenfield 0
Race

Final
Melchester Rovers v Cranville United

MAY '72 – But first Rovers had a win-at-all costs game in the League against Fordhampton – the week before the Cup Final...

1971-72

THE MELCHESTER SKIPPER NODDED THE BALL DOWN TO JUMBO TRUDGEON'S FEET.

IT'S A GOAL!

ROVERS HAVE GONE IN FRONT!

BEN ALLOWED HIMSELF TO SMILE FOR THE FIRST TIME THAT AFTERNOON.

THAT'S MADE THINGS LOOK A LOT MORE HOPEFUL.

DON'T COUNT YOUR CHICKENS, BEN. FORDHAMPTON AREN'T LETTING US OFF THE HOOK THAT EASILY.

ROY SET AN EXAMPLE TO HIS ATTACK WITH EVEN MORE DETERMINED EFFORTS.

COME ON, ROY. WE MUST HAVE ANOTHER.

AND AS IF TO PROVE TAFFY'S WORDS...

THEY'VE EQUALISED!

ROVERS ARE BACK WHERE THEY STARTED.

ROY'S LOST THE BALL!

BUT LOOK AT THAT BACK-PASS. THAT'S DANGEROUS!

HARASSED AND UNDER PRESSURE, THE FORDHAMPTON DEFENDER HAD TRIED TO GET THE BALL BACK TO HIS GOAL-KEEPER.

LOOK AT VERNON ELIOT RUNNING IN!

IT WAS A GOAL!

TWO-ONE TO ROVERS!

THAT SHOULD SETTLE IT.

AND WHEN THE ROVERS REACHED THE DRESSING ROOM THERE WAS EXCITING NEWS.

I'VE JUST HAD THE FINAL SCORE FROM MOLTON. THEY WENT DOWN TWO-ONE.

THAT MEANS WE'VE OVERTAKEN THEM, AND THEY CAN'T CATCH UP!

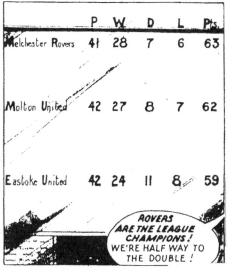

	P	W	D	L	Pts.
Melchester Rovers	41	28	7	6	63
Molton United	42	27	8	7	62
Eastoke United	42	24	11	8	59

ROVERS ARE THE LEAGUE CHAMPIONS! WE'RE HALF WAY TO THE DOUBLE!

ROY of the ROVERS

HIS PERSISTENCE PAID OFF.

HE'S SCORED!

WHAT A GOAL!

MELCHESTER ROVERS 1   CRANVILLE UNITED 1

WELL DONE, EDDIE.

STEADY ON. I THINK I'VE WRENCHED MY KNEE.

AFTER A FEW MINUTES, MANAGER BEN GALLOWAY SAW TRAINER TAFFY MORGAN SIGNALLING.

GET YOUR TRACK SUIT OFF, CHALKIE — EDDIE'S HURT.

CHALKIE WHITE JOINED THE LINE-UP.

HARD LUCK ON ROVERS, HAVING TO MAKE A SUBSTITUTION.

CHALKIE WON'T LET THEM DOWN.

ROY SOON GAINED POSSESSION OF THE BALL...

THAT'S IT, ROY — TAKE IT THROUGH...

YOURS, CHALKIE!

ROVERS ARE BEGINNING TO PLAY LIKE REAL CHAMPIONS!

CHALKIE SENT A HIGH CROSS-FIELD PASS TO VERNON, WHO HEADED IT DOWN IN FRONT OF JUMBO TRUDGEON.

ROVERS HAVE GOT CRANVILLE IN TROUBLE AGAIN!

JUMBO'S SHOT GAVE THE CRANVILLE KEEPER NO CHANCE.

IT'S THERE!

TWO-ONE TO ROVERS!

BUT THEN THE PACE OF THE GAME BEGAN TO SLOW.

ROVERS SEEM TO HAVE EASED OFF.

MAYBE THEY'RE JUST CONTENT TO COAST ALONG UNTIL HALF-TIME.

1971-72

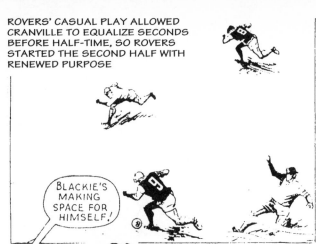

ROVERS' CASUAL PLAY ALLOWED CRANVILLE TO EQUALIZE SECONDS BEFORE HALF-TIME, SO ROVERS STARTED THE SECOND HALF WITH RENEWED PURPOSE

BLACKIE'S MAKING SPACE FOR HIMSELF!

BLACKIE'S THROUGH!

THIS MUST BE A GOAL.

THERE'S ONLY THE GOALIE TO BEAT!

THE SHOT WAS TOO HURRIED.

OVER THE BAR!

ROVERS WILL NEVER HAVE A BETTER CHANCE THAN THAT!

QUICK ANTICIPATION BY ROY PREVENTED CRANVILLE FROM GETTING ANY ADVANTAGE FROM THEIR GOAL KICK.

TRY AGAIN, BLACKIE.

THIS TIME BLACKIE STEADIED HIMSELF BEFORE SENDING IN HIS SHOT.

IT'S A GOAL!

THREE-TWO TO ROVERS!

CRANVILLE WEREN'T READY TO ACCEPT DEFEAT.

IT ISN'T OVER YET.

CRANVILLE PULLED BACK FROM BEHIND ONCE. THEY COULD DO IT AGAIN.

TUBBY WAS FORCED TO PUNCH A FIERCE SHOT OVER THE BAR.

CORNER!

MERVYN ON UP IN THE RIGHT DIRECTION

AUGUST '72

Chalky White, Chris Dylan and Eddie Eager, were transferred for reasons Roy Race explained to the Gazette, "The young players have a better chance of developing their careers playing in the first teams of other sides, not in the reserves nor sitting on the subs' bench at Rovers."

With two wonderfully taken goals from Race and Trudgeon, Rovers kicked off the 1972/73 league season with a win over their crosstown rivals...
Melchester Rovers 2   Shermall Athletic 0

SEPTEMBER '72

FORMER ROVERS' WINGER TONY STORME WAS APPOINTED COACH. STORME, A LIEUTENANT IN THE ARMY AS WELL AS A ROVERS' PLAYER, HAD LEFT MELCHESTER TO TAKE UP AN OVERSEAS ARMY POST.

Rovers' current winger Terry West wrongly feared that Tony Storme had arrived to take his place and went missing.

In their first matches after Storme's homecoming, Rovers continued their winning ways, even without West.

Melchester Rovers 2   Highwood Athletic 0
Trudgeon, Race

Weston Athletic 0   Melchester Rovers 2
Race, Trudgeon

Terry West, who had been involved in secret talks, was signed by Eastoke United, leaving Rovers in dire need of a replacement winger.

The Rovers' management team looked at a number of potential replacement wingers. From a shortlist of international players, there was only one choice...

NOV '72 – Rovers signed Cranville and England right-winger, Mervyn Wallace for a club record fee. Wallace impressed immediately on his debut, scoring both goals in Rovers' two-nil victory over Kingsbay in the league.

MERVYN'S FIRST AGAINST KINGSBAY ON HIS DEBUT FOR ROVERS.

NOV '72 – European Cup 2nd Round,
1st leg   Rovers 1   Hansberg [W. Ger.] 0
Eliot

DEC '72 – European Cup, 2nd round
2nd leg   Hansberg 0   Melchester Rovers 2
Warner, Gray
(Rovers win 3-0 on agg.)

JAN '73 – FA Cup, 3rd Round
Molton United 2   Melchester Rovers 1
Race

FEB '73 – European Cup, 3rd Round
1st Leg   Rovers 1   Real Montana [Spain] 1
Trudgeon

MAR '73 – European Cup, 3rd Round
2nd Leg   Real Montana 1   Rovers 3
Race, Wallace 2
(Rovers win 4-1 on agg.)

MERVYN WALLACE SCORES HIS SECOND GOAL, CLINCHING VICTORY OVER REAL MONTANA IN THE EUROPEAN CUP.

APR '73 – European Cup Semi-final
1st leg   Rovers 1   Terino [Italy] 0
Race

MAY '73 – European Cup Semi-final
2nd Leg   Terino 0   Melchester Rovers 2
Race, Gray
(Rovers win 3-0 on agg.)

ROY PUTS ROVERS INTO THE FINAL. MERVYN PROVED HE COULD MAKE, AS WELL AS TAKE, SCORING OPPORTUNITIES.

MAY '73 EUROPEAN CUP FINAL

MELCHESTER ROVERS
V
CORADOS [Portugal]

1972-73

ROVERS' FORM IN THE OPENING MINUTES OF THE GAME DELIGHTED THEIR COACH, TONY STORME. BUT MANAGER BEN GALLOWAY WAS MORE CAUTIOUS...

OUR LADS ARE GETTING A LOT MORE OF THE BALL THAN CORADOS, BEN.

BUT IT'S WHAT THEY'RE ALLOWED TO DO WITH IT THAT COUNTS AND CORADOS SEEM TO HAVE DONE THEIR HOMEWORK ON US.

VERNON ELIOT RAN THE BALL INTO THE MIDDLE, AND JUMBO TRUDGEON OVERLAPPED HIM TO FILL THE SPACE ON THE WING.

BUT THEIR BACK FOUR AREN'T BEING DRAWN INTO LEAVING GAPS. JUMBO'S STILL BEING WELL-MARKED!

VERNON'S ATTEMPT TO SET UP A CHANCE FOR ROY WAS FOILED BY TIGHT MARKING.

THIS IS GOING TO BE A REAL BATTLE OF SKILLS. WE'RE UP AGAINST ONE OF THE CLEVEREST SIDES IN EUROPE!

LOFTY PEAK CAME FORWARD TO CHECK A DANGEROUS BREAK.

...AND IT LOOKS AS IF THEY HAVE STUDIED LOFTY PRETTY CLOSELY, TOO!

LOFTY'S ONE SMALL WEAKNESS IS THAT HE TENDS TO SLOW DOWN WHEN HE'S MADE TO TURN ON HIS LEFT FOOT — AND THEY'RE EXPLOITING IT.

LITTLE GEOFF GILES, IN SPITE OF A POWERFUL TACKLE, GOT THE BALL OUT OF DANGER.

OOOF!

GEOFF'S BURLY OPPONENT HOISTED HIM BACK TO HIS FEET IN A RATHER PATRONISING WAY.

LO SIENTO, AMIGO.

GEOFF REACTED WITH QUICK INDIGNATION.

KEEP YOUR HANDS TO YOURSELF, MATE!

SORRY, NO SPIKKA INGLEES!

BEN SCOWLED. I BET THERE'S NOTHING THEY DON'T KNOW ABOUT GEOFF'S RECORD FOR LOSING HIS TEMPER. THEY'RE TRYING TO GET HIM RATTLED!

CORADOS MOUNTED ANOTHER DETERMINED ATTACK.

CORADOS ARE THROUGH!

IT LOOKS BAD FOR ROVERS!

TUBBY HURLED HIMSELF DOWN IN A BRAVE EFFORT TO PUT THE STRIKER OFF HIS SHOT...

HE COULDN'T HOLD IT!

ONCE AGAIN IT WAS GEOFF WHO GOT ROVERS OUT OF TROUBLE.

WELL DONE, GEOFF!

THAT WAS A NARROW ESCAPE FOR ROVERS!

GEOFF'S OPPONENT GAVE HIM A PAT ON THE HEAD.

BRAVO, AMIGO!

I TOLD YOU BEFORE — STOP DOING THAT!

NO SPIKKA INGLEES!

IT LOOKS AS IF ROY IS WARNING GEOFF NOT TO LET HIS TEMPER GET THE BETTER OF HIM.

HE'S DELIBERATELY IRRITATING YOU, GEOFF. IF YOU LOSE YOUR TEMPER, YOU'LL MAKE MISTAKES!

A FEW MOMENTS LATER, GEOFF — RUNNING TO TAKE A THROW-IN — SPOKE HURRIEDLY TO ANDY CROYDON.

IF WE'RE QUICK, THIS COULD GIVE US A BREAK. GO DEEP, AND WE'LL TRY TO PUSH IT THROUGH TO ROY.

THE MOVE DIDN'T SUCCEED, BUT GEOFF LEARNT SOMETHING FROM IT.

THAT CHAP DOES UNDERSTAND ENGLISH. HE OBVIOUSLY KNEW WHAT I SAID TO ANDY. THAT GIVES ME AN IDEA. I KNOW HOW TO HANDLE HIM NOW!

1972-73

WELL ROY, SO FAR THEY SEEM TO HAVE PLAYED THIS STRICTLY ACCORDING TO A PRE-MATCH PLAN. THEY'VE GOT TACTICS WORKED OUT FOR EACH ONE OF US.

MELCHESTER ROVERS v CORADOS [Portugal]

YES, THEY'RE CONCENTRATING ON STOPPING US FROM SCORING, WHILE WAITING FOR A SUDDEN, UNEXPECTED BREAK TO SNATCH A GOAL OF THEIR OWN.

GEOFF SPOKE QUIETLY TO ROY AND BLACKIE.

THAT BLOKE'S BEEN DOING HIS BEST TO NEEDLE ME... HE PRETENDS HE DOESN'T UNDERSTAND ENGLISH, BUT I'VE GOT A PLAN TO TURN THE TABLES ON HIM.

WHEN THE TEAMS CAME OUT FOR THE SECOND HALF, GEOFF'S TORMENTOR GAVE HIM A MOCK-FRIENDLY PAT...

I WARN YOU! IF YOU DO THAT ONCE MORE...

COACH TONY STORME TURNED ANXIOUSLY TO BEN GALLOWAY, ROVERS' MANAGER.

NO SPIKKA INGLEES.

GEOFF'S LETTING HIMSELF BE GOT AT AGAIN!

NOT THIS TIME. HE'S PUTTING ON AN ACT!

THE HALF WAS A FEW MINUTES OLD WHEN GEOFF PUT HIS PLAN INTO ACTION...

ROY—TO YOU— ON HIS RIGHT.

THE OPPONENT, AS GEOFF HAD SUSPECTED, UNDERSTOOD, AND ANTICIPATED THE BALL COMING THROUGH ON HIS RIGHT.

HE FELL FOR IT. THAT'LL TEACH HIM TO PRETEND HE CAN'T UNDERSTAND A WORD I SAY.

GEOFF'S SURPRISE MOVE LED TO MERVYN WALLACE TESTING THE CORADOS GOALIE WITH A TREMENDOUS SHOT.

KEEP UP THE PRESSURE, ROVERS.

THAT WAS NEARLY A GOAL.

1972-73

GEOFF AND HIS RIVAL WERE SOON IN OPPOSITION AGAIN.

COME ON, ROY. WE'LL DO IT RIGHT THIS TIME.

THE CORADOS PLAYER HESITATED UNCERTAINLY, GIVING GEOFF TIME TO MAKE AN UNEXPECTED MOVE.

GEOFF'S *BACKHEELED* IT TO *ANDY!*

RUNNING ON, GEOFF GOT IN POSITION TO USE HIS HEAD TO ANDY'S CHIPPED PASS.

NOW THEN, ROY...

ROY SNAPPED UP THE NODDED DOWN BALL WITH DEADLY EFFECT.

IT'S *THERE!*

ROVERS ARE IN FRONT!

ROY'S SCORED!

IT WAS THE TURN OF GEOFF'S OPPONENT TO LOOK BAD-TEMPERED!

NO SPIKKA INGLEES, EH?

THE NEXT TIME THE TWO PLAYERS CLASHED, GEOFF WON THE BALL WITH A CUNNING SWERVE, BUT...

OOOF!

BOOO! FOUL, REF!

HE'S GETTING A WARNING!

I SHOULD THINK SO, TOO!

TONY STORME REALISED THAT THE CORADOS MANAGER HAD MADE A QUICK DECISION.

THEY'VE DECIDED TO BRING HIM OFF BEFORE HE GETS HIMSELF INTO WORSE TROUBLE.

WELL, IT LOOKS AS IF OUR GEOFF HAS WON THE BATTLE OF NERVES! GOOD FOR HIM!

UNDETERRED, CORADOS CONTINUED TO PRESS HARD.

CORADOS ARE PLAYING IT VERY THIN AT THE BACK.

THEY'VE NO *CHOICE*...TIME'S RUNNING OUT...THEY NEED EVERY MAN UP IN ATTACK IF THEY'RE TO GET AN EQUALISER.

1972-73

AFTER ROY AND BLACKIE HAD SEEN OFF THE CHALLENGE OF THE PORTUGUESE CHAMPIONS, THE TWO PALS JOINED FORCES FOR ENGLAND, IN AN EMOTIONAL 2-0 WIN OVER ITALY, IN ROME. TRUE TO FORM, ROY SET BLACKIE UP FOR ENGLAND'S FIRST, AND BLACKIE REPAID THE DEBT, FOR ROY TO RAM HOME THE SECOND GOAL.

THE "LEAP"-YEAR OF THE CAT!

AUG '73 – HAVING DONE THE DOUBLE THE PREVIOUS SEASON, ROVERS STARTED THE NEW SEASON WITH A NEW LOOK STRIP AND A NEW MANAGEMENT SET-UP. BEN GALLOWAY HAD BEEN PROMOTED TO GENERAL MANAGER, WHILE TEAM COACH TONY STORME WAS PROMOTED TO FIRST TEAM MANAGER.

THE ROVERS' LINE UP FOR THE NEW SEASON PROUDLY SHOWED OFF THEIR NEW STRIP AND THE EUROPEAN CUP...
BACK ROW: RALPH DERRY (2), MERVYN WALLACE (7), VERNON ELIOT (11)
MIDDLE ROW: BEN GALLOWAY (GEN MGR.), TUBBY MORTON (1), GEOFF GILES (4), LOFTY PEAK (6), TONY STORME (TEAM MGR.)
FRONT ROW: JUMBO TRUDGEON (10), JIMMY SLADE (5), ROY RACE (9 & CAPT.), BLACKIE GRAY (8), NOEL BAXTER (3)

OCTOBER '73

The new look did not bring Rovers good fortune in the League, as the reigning champions found it very difficult going and were well out of contention to repeat their league success by the end of the year.

To make matters worse, veteran goal-keeper Tubby Morton broke his leg in the first game of the season against Carford City. Reserve 'keeper Peter Baker was badly injured in a car crash before he had a chance to replace Morton, so manager Tony Storme brought in the precociously agile Charlie "The Cat" Carter.

NOVEMBER '73

With the continued spate of injuries and poor results, many of the players felt the new strip was jinxed. The more the players talked of the jinx, the worse their performances became.

It took some research by captain Roy Race to show that Rovers' 1907 F.A. Cup winning side wore a very similar strip to the new kit.

In Rovers' next game, freed of the jinx, they destroyed old rivals Portdean City 5-0 to record the club's first league win of the season.

DECEMBER '73

Despite finally debunking the jinx, captain Roy Race himself suffered a serious injury, when he was shot in the leg by Colonel Chadwick, while trying to quell a demonstration against a local by-pass scheme that Jumbo Trudgeon had somehow become embroiled in.

The injury wasn't as bad as first thought and Roy was soon back playing.

Despite a mini-recovery in the league, to be placed midway over Christmas, Rovers' form in the cup competitions was much more promising....

1973-74

MAR '74 – LEAGUE CUP Results:

2nd Round
Lenfield 3   Melchester Rovers 4
Race (3), Gray

3rd Round
Wakeford [2nd Div] 1   Melchester Rovers 1
Race

Replay
Melchester Rovers 2   Wakeford 0
Race, Trudgeon

4th Round
Melchester Rovers 1   Cranville United 0
Race

5th Round
Melchester Rovers 2   Brentwich 1
Race (2)

Semi-final
1st Leg   Rovers 0 Carford City 1
2nd Leg   Carford City 1   Rovers 2
Race, Giles
(2-2 on agg. Rovers win on away goals rule)

League Cup Final at Wembley Stadium
Melchester Rovers 1   Highwood 0

**MELCHESTER RADIO REPORTED
THE GAME-WINNING GOAL,**
"Race pounced on a loose back pass and, off-balance, placed the ball wide of the onrushing keeper, which meant Roy had scored in each round of the League Cup."

This wasn't to be Rovers' last trip to Wembley this season....

ROVER'S ROAD TO WEMBLEY...

Melchester Rovers'
F.A. Cup Results:

3rd Round
Walford Town 0   Rovers 3
Slade, Farmer (og), Race

4th Round
Rovers 3   Molton United 0
Giles (2), Race

5th Round
Weston Athletic 0   Rovers 1
Race

6th Round
Rovers 1   Crampton 0
Trudgeon,

Semi-final
Rovers 3   Bridgewell 1
Baxter, Race (2)

F.A. CUP FINAL

MELCHESTER ROVERS
v BURNDEAN
at Wembley Stadium

LED BY THEIR BRILLIANT SKIPPER, ROY RACE, FIRST DIVISION MELCHESTER ROVERS WERE CHASING A UNIQUE CUP-DOUBLE. ALREADY, THE LEAGUE CUP WAS 'IN THE BAG', AND NOW THE ROVERS WERE FIGHTING IT OUT WITH BURNDEAN, IN THE FINAL OF THE F.A. CUP...A GAME WHICH HAD BEEN DUBBED 'THE GOLDEN FINAL', BECAUSE THE WINNING TEAM STOOD TO COLLECT £5,000 PER MAN. IN THEIR EAGERNESS TO SCORE, THE ROVERS HAD LEFT THEMSELVES WIDE OPEN, AND WERE TRAILING BY ONE GOAL!

1973-74

MELCHESTER ROVERS LINE UP	4 GEOFF GILES	8 BLACKIE GRAY
1 TUBBY MORTON	5 JIMMY SLADE	9 ROY RACE
2 RALPH DERRY	6 LOFTY PEAK	10 JUMBO TRUDGEON
3 NOEL BAXTER	7 MERV WALLACE	11 VERNON ELIOT

AT HALF-TIME, BEFORE ROY COULD GIVE HIS TEAM THE NECESSARY KICK IN THE BACKSIDE, DIRECTOR TED MANNING STEPPED IN TO INCREASE HIS CONTROVERSIAL £5,000 WIN-BONUS TO AN EXTRA £2,000 PER MAN PER GOAL.

RELUCTANTLY ROY HAD TO ACCEPT THESE BONUSES, BUT HE HAD PROMISED HIS SHARE, IF ANY, TO A LOCAL YOUTH CLUB. THE ORIGINAL "BOUNTY" HAD UPSET ROY - IT HAD TAKEN THE PLAYERS' MINDS OFF THE GAME; INCENSED AT THE INCREASED REWARD HE STORMED OUT TO START THE SECOND HALF. ROY'S ANGER SPILLED OVER ON TO THE PITCH, WHERE A SERIES OF RASH TACKLES ALMOST SAW HIS NAME IN THE REFEREE'S BOOK — ONLY ROY'S EXEMPLARY PAST PLAYING RECORD PERSUADED THE REFEREE TO DEFER A BOOKING AND ISSUE A STERN VERBAL CAUTION.. CHASTENED, ROY WENT BACK TO DOING WHAT HE DOES BEST....

THAT'S NOT SUCH A SILLY SHOT AFTER ALL...ROY SPOTTED THAT THE BURNDEAN GOALIE HAD COME OFF HIS LINE!

THE DEADLY-ACCURATE BALL STRUCK THE UNDERSIDE OF THE CROSS-BAR, AND NEXT MOMENT...

IT'S *THERE*!

BURNDEAN 1 MELCHESTER ROVERS 1!

DELIGHTED ROVERS CONVERGED ON ROY!

GOOD OLD ROY!

WHAT A SHOT! GREAT EFFORT, SKIPPER!

HOLD IT! GO EASY ON THE CONGRATULATIONS...

I'M NOT SURE IF YOU ARE CHEERING BECAUSE I'VE JUST EARNED YOU ANOTHER TWO THOUSAND POUNDS, OR BECAUSE WE'RE BACK IN WITH A GOOD CHANCE OF PULLING OFF THE CUP DOUBLE...!

AS FAR AS I'M CONCERNED, ALL THAT MATTERS IS WINNING THE CUP... WHICH MEANS *STOPPING BURNDEAN*, AS WELL AS SCORING GOALS!

AS THE GAME RESTARTED...

I WANT *TWO* MEN ON THAT WINGER! TAKE HIM OUT, JIMMY!

I'LL COVER HIM, ROY...!

AS THE BURNDEAN WINGER SLIPPED PAST JIMMY SLADE...

LOFTY'S GOT IT! GREAT TACKLE!

IT LOOKS AS IF ROY HAS SHAMED THEM INTO PLAYING LIKE A *TEAM* AGAIN!

MAY '74

Roy's scintillating two goal strike helped ensure Rovers completed a historic League and FA Cup double, which their early season league form had not suggested possible.

Under team manager Tony Storme, Rovers had struggled all season to make any impact in the league, but managed to find their real form in both the major domestic cup competitions.

Through the determined efforts of team captain Roy Race and the rest of the Rovers' players, the Melchester Stadium cleaning staff had another busy off-season keeping the silverware sparkling.

1973-74

GOVERNOR OF THE RANK OF ENGLAND

AUGUST '74

Legendary goalkeeper Tubby Morton resumed training after two years lay-off through injury. With first team goalie Charlie 'The Cat' Carter torn between football and a career as a pop singer, Tubby made his first-team return in Rovers 1-1 draw with Barnley in August.

SEP '74 – European Cup-Winners' Cup, Preliminary Round

1st Leg	Rovers	1	Zeeden [Holland]	0
	Race			
2nd Leg	Zeeden	1	Rovers	2
			Race (2)	

(Rovers win 3-1 on agg.)

ROY'S SECOND AGAINST ZEEDEN IN THE SECOND LEG

During the second leg victory, Tubby Morton was badly hurt, and as a result of this long-term injury, he was appointed the manager of Rovers' 'A' Team. Charlie 'The Cat' Carter took over as Rovers' first-team goalkeeper.

NOVEMBER '74

In the next round, Rovers faced old rivals and the current Cup holders, Carford City, to decide who would carry British hopes through to the Second Round.

European Cup-Winners' Cup, 1st Round

1st Leg	Rovers	2	Carford City	0
	Gray (2)			
2nd Leg	Carford City	1	Rovers	1
			Wallace	

(Rovers win 3-1 on agg.)

DECEMBER '74

STORME'S STRANGE JUGGLING ACT

Storme's decision to draft circus juggler Sammy Spangler in place of Rovers' injured Jumbo Trudgeon, must be the most bizarre signing in football history. Storme is convinced that soccer novice Spangler's undeniable ball-skills, will be effectively translated on the soccer pitch.

JANUARY '75

Melchester Rovers 4   Highwood 4

Sammy Spangler today added another trick to his repertoire, a disappearing act and, against Highwood, it snatched certain victory from Rovers' grasp. Thanks to an opener from Jimmy Slade and a superb Roy Race hat-trick, Rovers had been four-nil up against Highwood. But Race was injured and his replacement Spangler was nowhere to be seen. With Rovers down to ten men, Highwood pulled back all four goals against a weary and overstretched Rovers. In latching himself to the unreliable Spangler, Tony Storme is putting more than his reputation on the line.

JANUARY '75

FA Cup 3rd Round
Sleeford Town 2   Melchester Rovers 1

In the biggest upset in FA Cup history, Melchester Rovers have stumbled in the FA Cup Third Round at the hands of non-league minnows, Sleeford Town. Sleeford Park was packed to overflowing and the crowd had spilled onto the pitch halting the game for several minutes. Rovers' new signing, ex-circus juggler Sammy Spangler looked bewildered in the fervent cauldron and was totally out of his depth. Two soft Sleeford goals later and Rovers looked out of it. But a Mervyn Wallace goal brought Rovers back into the game and in the closing seconds Lofty Peak burst through and headed the ball in the back of the net, but it was disallowed. The jinx had struck again, Rovers were out of the cup.

JAN '75 – After this humiliating defeat, Tony Storme, unable to face the fans' and Ben Galloway's wrath disappeared.

JANUARY '75

ROY RACE – MANAGER

From the ashes of FA Cup defeat and the embarrassing vanishing act of Rovers' manager Tony Storme, a phoenix of hope has arisen at battle-weary Melchester. Roy Race has accepted the directors' invitation to become player-manager.

Director Sam Butler said, "We need someone who holds the trust and confidence of the players. A man who can inspire them to pick up the pieces and start winning again. That man is Roy Race."

"I'LL DO IT MY WAY"

says Roy Race

Commenting on his delay in accepting the board's invitation to become player-manager, Roy Race told the Gazette, "It wasn't an easy decision and I thought long and hard about the offer. Tony had disappeared and I didn't want to step into a 'dead man's' shoes. We were bombarded by the media, eager for my answer, but I needed to think it over. Two things helped me decide – sackfuls of mail from supporters backing me all the way and the rapidly plummeting morale among the players, who felt leaderless. I knew it would take an iron hand to pick the lads off the floor and they have given 100% support to let me do it my way."

FEB '75

Melchester Rovers v Castledene

Two-nil down at half-time, Roy's honeymoon as the 'fan's choice' for manager was over. Questions were being asked about his ability to handle the added pressure.

As Roy left the pitch, at half-time, a masked man, in the crowd, handed him a note, "STOP FUSSING LIKE A MOTHER-HEN AND PLAY YOUR OWN GAME." Roy recognised Tony Storme's hand-writing - the ex-coach, still in hiding, was still looking out for the Rovers. The note motivated Roy.

As the team ran out for the second half, he vowed "No more fancy stuff! From now on I'm just a plain old-fashioned centre forward! It's goals or nothing!"

There was no holding Roy, as he took the game by the scruff of the neck and launched attack after blistering attack on the shocked Castledene defenders. First with a left foot rocket and then a header past a flailing goalkeeper, Roy drew Rovers level. But Roy was not finished...

By the end of ninety minutes, Roy had scored all four of Rovers' goals and cemented his position as team manager.

With Roy firmly in command, on and off the pitch, Rovers looked forward to their next European Cup-Winners' Cup opponents...

MAR '75 – Quarter-final

1st Leg	Rovers	1	Zarnov [Vlatnia]	0
	Race			
2nd Leg	Zarnov	2	Rovers	2
			Race (2)	

(Rovers win 3-2 on agg.)

MAY '75 – Semi-final

1st Leg	Rovers	4	Durmstadt [W. Ger]	0
	Gray, Race (2), Slade			
2nd Leg	Durmstadt	3	Rovers	1
			Race	

(Rovers win 5-3 on agg.)

MAY '75 – Tony Storme came out of hiding to confirm that he had left football to concentrate on running his successful sports centre business with his brother Brian.

1975 EUROPEAN CUP-WINNERS' CUP FINAL
MELCHESTER ROVERS v NIARKOS [GREECE]
AT HAMPDEN PARK, SCOTLAND

Niarkos were the surprise finalists, after upsetting mighty Atletico Tandora in the semi-final. But Roy hadn't done his homework properly. He had briefed his side fully on Tandora, but he knew nothing about his shock opponents Niarkos, a mistake which could now cost him his job.

Roy's only information came from Niarkos' fans outside the stadium, who boasted about their attacking left-back Florina and strikers Populus and Andreus. Roy's ability to use these shreds of information to plan his tactics, before kick-off, was going to be tested to the full.

Seconds after kick-off, Roy's 'knowledge' had helped prevent an early Niarkos goal. But as he picked up the ball from Charlie Carter's throw, his dream of winning the European Cup-Winners' Cup at his first attempt as manager, was on the brink of becoming a nightmare.

ROY OF THE ROVERS

COULD ROY'S PLANNING BRING ROVERS VICTORY IN THEIR CUP-WINNERS' CUP FINAL?

1974-75

LEFT TO RIGHT, BACK ROW: JUMBO TRUDGEON, BLACKIE GRAY, CHARLIE CARTER, VERNON ELIOT, LOFTY PEAK, GRAHAM SHAW; FRONT ROW: NOEL BAXTER, MERVYN WALLACE, GEOFF GILES, JIMMY SLADE, RALPH DERRY; LEFT FOREGROUND: ROY RACE (PLAYER-MANAGER)

1974-75

BOOTED AND SUITED!

JULY '75

Just before England's European Nations Cup game against France, Roy had secretly helped his old friend, Jules Bernard – the wealthy star of the French side – to overcome two men who had kidnapped Jules' young nephew.

Roy had started the match without knowing if Jules and his nephew were safe. Mid-way through the second half, Jules appeared on the sideline and took his place on the pitch. He managed to get a message to Roy that everything was fine. A very relieved Roy Race then turned on the old magic....

After a disastrous start to the season, Rovers lost their first five league games. The team made a spirited comeback inspired by their record signing Duncan McKay from Portdean City with a morale-boosting draw against his old side.

McKay provided the much-needed backbone that Rovers had been lacking.

Rovers performed more consistently in the League Cup...

2nd Round
Melchester Rovers 1   Selbridge [2nd Div] 0
Gray
3rd Round
Eastgate 0   Melchester Rovers 5
Gray (2), Giles, Eliot, Race

4th Round
Melchester Rovers 1   Tarbury [3rd Div] 0
Gray
5th Round
Melchester Rovers 4   Carford City 2
Race, Gray (2), Peak

Semi-final
1st Leg   Hansfield [2nd Div] 3   Rovers 0
2nd Leg   Melchester Rovers v Hansfield...

FOR THE MOMENT, ROY FORGOT ABOUT HIS INJURY!

ONE MORE GOAL AND WE'RE LEVEL ON AGGREGATE SCORES!

AND THEN THEY'LL *HAVE* TO COME OUT AT US!

LET'S HAVE ANOTHER, LADS!

BUT THE INEXPERIENCE OF MELCHESTER'S YOUNGSTERS...PLUS A LARGE SLICE OF LUCK...CAME TO HANSFIELD'S RESCUE!

OOOH! HARD LUCK! BLACKIE HIT THE POST!

JUST OVER THE BAR...

AND WITH ONLY TWO MINUTES LEFT!

LOFTY, IT'S ALL OR NOTHING NOW ...GET UP THERE! TRY AND USE YOUR HEIGHT!

OKAY, ROY...

AND, ALMOST IMMEDIATELY...

AA-AAAACH!

LOFTY'S RIGHT IN THE THICK OF THE ACTION!

THE GOALIE COULD ONLY PUNCH IT OUT!

DUNCAN McKAY'S SHOT WAS STOPPED ON THE LINE...

THE BALL'S REBOUNDING TO VERNON ELIOT!

MELCHESTER *MUST* SCORE!

BUT EVEN AS VERNON TOOK AIM...

THERE'S THE FINAL WHISTLE ...IT'S ALL OVER!

HANSFIELD ARE IN THE FINAL!

ROY WAS THE FIRST TO CONGRATULATE THE HANSFIELD MANAGER!

ROY, IF YOU HADN'T BEEN INJURED, IT MIGHT HAVE BEEN A VERY DIFFERENT RESULT!

BUT WE'LL NEVER KNOW, WILL WE, ARCHIE? JUST MAKE SURE YOU WIN THAT CUP, THAT'S ALL!

AND AS FOR YOU LOT...DON'T LOOK SO SHATTERED! THERE'S STILL THE LEAGUE, AND THE F.A. CUP!

WE'RE BOUND TO WIN *SOMETHING*, EH, BLACKIE?

MAR '76

Despite being sensationally knocked out the League Cup, Rovers were still well placed in the league and were always a force to reckon with in the F.A. Cup.

Apart from a possible league and cup double, looming on the horizon was another important date for Roy Race – his wedding day.

The lucky lady being Penny Laine – Ben Galloway's secretary – who had managed to snare one of the country's most eligible bachelors. Over the past few months, Roy had found Penny's help and companionship vital in his dual role as player-manager. So marriage seemed to be a natural progression to their burgeoning relationship.

Rovers had started on yet another successful F.A. Cup run...

3rd Round
Melchester Rovers 6   Whitburn Spartan 0
Trudgeon (3), Slade, Gray, Wallace

This was Jumbo Trudgeon's last game for Rovers, being replaced by 19 year old Gerry Holloway. The fans would never forget Jumbo's years of pomp and majesty.

4th Round
Melchester Rovers 2   Railford [2nd Div] 0
Race, Holloway

5th Round
Dumpton Town 0   Melchester Rovers 4
Holloway (3), Peak

6th Round
Deans Park 1   Melchester Rovers 2
Gray, Race

Semi-final
Melchester Rovers 3   Sandford 0
Race (3)

Having made the cup final, Rovers suffered a shock 1-0 defeat to relegation-haunted Westhampton and could only finish runners-up to Tynecastle, in the league.

1976 F. A. Cup Final at Wembley
Melchester Rovers v Oldfield

A MOMENT LATER!

THERE'S THE WHISTLE — IT'S ALL OVER! OLDFIELD HAVE WON THE CUP!

I D-DON'T BELIEVE IT! WE'VE FINISHED SECOND... AGAIN!

ROY TRIED HARD NOT TO SHOW HIS DISAPPOINTMENT!

SORRY, RACEY...BUT SOMEONE'S GOT TO LOSE!

THE TROUBLE IS, JOHNNY, IT ALWAYS SEEMS TO BE MELCHESTER, JUST LATELY! ANYWAY, TAKE CARE OF THAT CUP FOR US...BECAUSE WE SHALL WANT IT BACK NEXT SEASON!

SO... HEADS UP, ROVERS! I DON'T WANT TO SEE ANY CUP-FINAL BLUES ON MY FINAL DAY OF FREEDOM!

FREEDOM?

GOSH, I ALMOST FORGOT! ROY'S GETTING MARRIED!

AND SOON...

GOOD LUCK, ROY!

THERE HE IS — GOOD OLD ROY!

DOESN'T HE LOOK GREAT!

GOOD LUCK!

PHEEEW! I ONLY SENT OUT TWO HUNDRED INVITATIONS, BUT THE WHOLE OF MELCHESTER HAS TURNED UP!

AN EVEN BIGGER CHEER RANG OUT, AS ROY AND HIS BRIDE, PENNY, CAME OUT AFTER THE CEREMONY!

OOOOHHH, DON'T THEY LOOK SMASHING!

THE ROVERS ARE FORMING A GUARD OF HONOUR!

GOOD LUCK

WELL, I CAN'T SAY THE SEASON HAS BEEN A COMPLETE LOSS, PENNY! HOW DOES IT FEEL TO BE MRS. RACE?

I'LL LET YOU KNOW IN ABOUT SIXTY YEARS TIME!

GOOD LUC

PENNY THREW HER BOUQUET TO THE CROWD...BUT ROY CHOSE AN AUTOGRAPHED FOOTBALL!

LET'S HOPE A YOUNGSTER GETS IT! IT MIGHT BE SOME KIND OF OMEN FOR HIM!

HE COULD BECOME A FUTURE STAR OF MELCHESTER ROVERS!

LATER, AT THE RECEPTION IN THE SUPPORTERS' CLUB AT MELCHESTER STADIUM!

GOOD LUCK ROY & PENNY

ROY, YOU STILL HAVEN'T TOLD US WHERE YOU TWO ARE GOING FOR YOUR HONEY-MOON!

AND I DON'T INTEND TO! WE'RE KEEPING OUR DESTINATION AN UTTER SECRET, TO MAKE SURE WE HAVE A COMPLETE BREAK! NO CAMERAS...NO REPORTERS...ABSOLUTELY NOTHING TO DO WITH FOOTBALL!

YOU HOPE! I'VE A FEELING YOU'D GET INVOLVED IN A FOOTBALL MATCH, IF WE GOT WASHED UP ON A DESERT ISLAND!

1975-76

A GOAL-A-GAME KEEPS THE GOAL-RUSH AFLAME!

SUPERMARKET CHAIN OFFERS £30,000 TO FIRST PLAYER TO SCORE 50 GOALS!!

What a way to start a new football season! £30,000 for the first player to score 50 League and Cup goals – and Melchester have three players capable of doing just that. Blackie Gray, Mervyn Wallace – and the bookies' favourite – Roy Race.

Race found the net 38 times in 54 games last season – in which Rovers reached the League Cup semi-finals, FA Cup Final and finished runners-up in the League. So, in order for a Rovers' player to score 50 goals, the team must have an excellent season in all three competitions. So the "goal-rush" can only be good for Melchester – and may the best man WIN!

WILLIAM HILLS ODDS
5/1	Roy Race	Melchester
7/1	Ben Webster	Tynecaster
	Eddie Hamilton	Gatesford
9/1	Johnny Hodges	Kingsbay
10/1	Mervyn Wallace	Melchester
	Blackie Gray	Melchester
12/1	Rex Stewart	Portdean

Unavailable for comment, Roy Race is soon to return from Brazil where he played for a Europe Select XI against a South America XI. Race, who broke off his honeymoon in Italy to represent Europe, was chosen as "Man of the Tournament" for his all-round performances. Married life appears to be agreeing with the Rovers' player-manager.

Knowing Roy Race, it wouldn't be surprising to find him ignoring the £30,000 goal-rush to devote his energies to getting Rovers off to a fast start in the League.

CHARITY PROMISE

In an attempt to deflect some of the pressure he is feeling from leading the £30,000 "goal-rush" Roy Race announced yesterday that if he is the first to reach 50 goals, he will donate the money to an unnamed charity. The Man with the Midas-boot (everything he touches turns to goal) has already scored 17 goals in eleven games and looks set to achieve the magical 50 well before the end of the season.

If Rovers keep up their blistering League form, having dropped only three points out of twenty-two, they could be looking to surpass the club's record unbeaten start to a season – 19 games (league and cup) set in 1957/58.

RECORD START!

Melchester Rovers 2   Tynecaster 0

Almost twenty years ago, Rovers went nineteen games undefeated to open the 1957/58 season. Yesterday, the current Rovers' side went one better – twenty games without a loss – defeating Tynecaster in the League Cup.

After three minutes, Roy Race notched his 25th goal of the season, with a diving header of such power, that he took off outside the six-yard box and ended up alongside the ball in the back of the net. In making the cross for the goal, Gerry Holloway received a bad knock and was replaced by Roger "Super-Sub" Dixon. Two goals in his last two appearances as sub, Dixon was mightily miffed at Roy Race for not letting him start the game. To Race's credit, Dixon struggled to last the remaining 87 minutes, but in true "Super-Sub" style, he popped up in the dying seconds to score the second goal.

ROVERS DUMPED OUT OF CUP!

League Cup, Semi-Final, 2nd leg:
Melchester Rovers 0   Swinford Town 0
(Agg 0-1)

Having lost their season's unbeaten record to Second Division Swinford Town in the first leg, Rovers allowed their bogey team to keep their noses in front. Despite a constant barrage of crosses and shots on the Swinford goal, the side languishing in the depths of Division Two, managed to keep the rampant Rovers at bay. Roy Race who has only scored a couple of goals in the last eight games finally got the ball into the net but moments after referee Mr Black had blown for full-time. Rovers now have to pick themselves up to prepare for Saturday's Fourth Round F.A. Cup match at Holverton.

F.A. CUP FOURTH ROUND V HOLVERTON.

FINAL SCORE – ROVERS 5   HOLVERTON 0
WALLACE (3), RACE (2)

CURRENT GOAL-RUSH STANDINGS

	Player	Team	Goals
1	Roy Race	Melchester	31
2	Eddie Hamilton	Gatesford	28
3	Rex Stewart	Portdean	26
4	Mervyn Wallace	Melchester	24
5	Ben Webster	Tynecaster	23
6	Johnny Hodges	Kingsbay	22
7	Frank Williams	Walford	20

ROVERS DUMPED OUT OF CUP – AGAIN!

F.A. Cup, 5th Rd:
Melchester Rovers 2   North Vale 3
Race, Wallace

AND... SURE ENOUGH!

SPORT
THE UNDEFEATED—MELCHESTER MAKE IT
ELEVEN IN A ROW..!

AND HERE'S THE GOAL THAT KEEPS ROY RACE OUT IN FRONT IN THE 'GOAL-RUSH'!

DAILY SPO...

I'M GOING TO GIVE IT ALL AWAY..

TEAM	PLAYED	WON	DRAWN	LOST	FOR	AGAINST	POINTS
MELCHESTER	11	8	3	0	37	9	19
TYNECASTER	11	7	2	2	29	13	16
BURNDEAN	11	6	4	1	27	15	16
KINGSBAY	11	6	4	1	26	19	16
PORTDEAN	10	6	3	1	24	17	15
CARFORD	11	6	2	3	21	11	14
MILBORO	11						

Melchester Rovers 4   Sandford 4

The cards were stacked against them, and the dice were loaded, but Rovers turned the tables on those who doubted they could do it. And do it they did, without five injured stars, Giles, Baxter, Eliot, Holloway and Carter. In their places were youngsters Gary Fane, Willy Edwards, Roger Dixon and Trevor Cassidy, with 45-year-old 'keeper Tubby Morton.

Dixon opened the scoring after Race had pounced on a back pass. Sandford were soon level when Barraclough struck home a twenty-yarder. Race put Rovers back in front with a drive from outside the box, but a Morton fumble gave the visitors another equalizer. Race converted a spot-kick, after Miller had handled, and Rovers were 3-2 up.

A Race back-pass set up Sandford's third, as Rovers buckled under the strain of the record. Before they could regroup, Morton was picking himself and the ball out the net.

With seconds left Wallace, tucked away Race's blocked blast to tie the game up. Deep into injury time, Bennett went past Peak and put in a low cross, that was met on the volley by Barraclough. The ball flashed towards the top right corner and was met by Morton, who tipped the ball onto the bar and over for a corner. As referee Mr Green blew for time, the Rovers team, to a man, mobbed their 'keeper – who had saved the day. In his first game in four years, Morton had extended Rovers' unbeaten League run to 29 games.

MAY '77 – After the unbeaten run, Rovers' win over Walford was their first in seven games...

Rovers 0   Everpool 1
Rovers 1   Portdean City 3
Wallace
Corstone City 5   Rovers 2
                    Gray, Dixon
Cranville City 1   Rovers 1
                    Slade
Rovers 2   Kingsbay 3
Wallace, Dixon
Linfield Athletic 2   Rovers 2
                    Gray, Wallace
Darnsley 3   Rovers 3
        Race (2), Wallace
Walford 1   Rovers 3

CURRENT GOAL-RUSH STANDINGS

Player	Goals
1 Roy Race Melchester	49
2 Eddie Hamilton Gatesford	48
3 Mervyn Wallace Melchester	47
4 Johnny Hodges Kingsbay	42
5 Rex Stewart Portdean	36
6 Ben Webster Tynecaster	33

MAY '77 – LEAGUE TABLE – TOP FOUR

	P	W	D	L	F	A	Pts	Goal Diff
Portdean City	42	27	10	5	106	34	64	+72
Kingsbay	42	26	11	5	115	47	63	+68
Melchester Rovers	41	26	11	4	137	70	63	+67
Tynecaster	41	24	11	6	107	55	59	+52

MAY '77 – With Gatesford playing in the F.A. Cup Final the following week, Eddie Hamilton was the only non-Rovers' player who had a shot at the £30,000 goal-rush. Both Roy and Mervyn could pip him to the pot of gold against Tynecaster in the last league game of the season.

In the dressing room after Rovers' last practice session of the season, Roy attempted to play down his own goal-rush chances and speak up for his inside-right...

SPOTLIGHT ON ROY RACE

By the late 1970s, Roy Race had become a fashionable media figure and the subject of many interviews and profiles.
One such appeared in *Gentleman's Monthly* magazine...

PERSONAL

Full Name: Roy Race

Birthplace: Melchester

Height: 6 foot 2 inches   *Weight:* 12 stone 3 pounds

Occupation: Player-Manager for Melchester Rovers

Previous jobs: None

Marital status: Married to Penny

Children: Twins – Roy Jnr and Melinda

Favourite car: Lotus

Favourite food(s): Trifle & smoked salmon (not together!)

Favourite drink: Hot, strong tea (I'm tea-total!)

CAREER

Favourite player: Blackie Gray (Melchester Rovers)

Most difficult opponent: Johnny Dexter (Danefield)

Most memorable match: My first for Melchester (1955)
and my first for England (1963)

Biggest career disappointment: Not playing more for my
country

Favourite other football team: Melchester Rovers' reserves

Biggest influence on career: Ben Galloway (Rovers' general-
al manager) and Alf Leeds (Rovers' scout)

Best goal scored: All 400+ of them

ENTERTAINMENT

Favourite film: The Arsenal Stadium Mystery

Favourite actor: Paul Newman

Favourite actress: Shirley Maclaine

Favourite singer(s): Barbra Streisand and Vic Damone

Favourite song: Melchester for the Cup!

Favourite TV show(s): Monty Python's Flying Circus, Match of the Day and Quiz Ball

Favourite reading material: Sports pages of newspapers and the Melchester match programme

Perfect night: At home with Penny and the twins

AMBITIONS

Career: To keep fit and healthy and playing, and winning for Melchester, and winning more caps for my country. Ultimately, playing in the World Cup Finals

Personal: To enjoy life with my family

If you were not a football player what would you do?: Buy a season ticket to Mel Park

Which personality would you most like to meet?: Pele

Favourite philosophical saying: 'If it isn't broke, why fix it?' and 'Practice makes perfect'

Favourite word or phrase: 'One-nil, Rovers!'

ENGLAND EXPECTS EVERY MANAGER TO DO HIS DUTY!

JANUARY '78

After the England manager was badly injured in a car crash, the Football Association named Roy Race as caretaker-manager of the national squad – for the upcoming friendly against Holland.

Roy only agreed to take the temporary position on his terms – and with his team. A last minute injury to a key player meant Roy had to play himself up front with some other well-known faces...

ROY RACE'S ENGLAND TEAM v HOLLAND AT WEMBLEY STADIUM

BACK ROW (L-R):
GEOFF GILES, CHARLIE CARTER, MERV WALLACE (ALL MELCHESTER ROVERS)

CENTRE ROW:
VERNON ELIOT, JIMMY SLADE (BOTH MELCHESTER ROVERS), JOHNNY DEXTER (REAL GRANPALA), MIKE BATESON, NIPPER LAWRENCE (BOTH BLACKPORT)

FRONT ROW:
NOEL BAXTER (MELCHESTER ROVERS), TREVOR FRANCIS (BIRMINGHAM CITY), ROY RACE (MELCHESTER ROVERS), MALCOLM MACDONALD (ARSENAL), LOFTY PEAK (MELCHESTER ROVERS)

MAR '78 – IN FRONT OF A SELL-OUT WEMBLEY STADIUM CROWD, THE NEW-LOOK ENGLAND TEAM TOOK A FEW MINUTES TO SETTLE DOWN AGAINST THE SILKILY SKILLED DUTCH SIDE. BUT, IT WASN'T LONG BEFORE "ROCKET" ROY RACE WAS LINKING UP WITH ARSENAL'S "GUNNER-RUNNER" MALCOLM MACDONALD...

ROY RACE AND HIS ENGLAND TEAM WERE UNABLE TO RECAPTURE THE LEAD BEFORE HALF-TIME, AND THE CARE-TAKER-MANAGER HAD A FEW WELL CHOSEN WORDS FOR HIS STAR SIDE DURING THE BREAK. ROY BROUGHT ON MELCHESTER ROVERS' DEFENSIVE MIDFIELDER GEOFF GILES FOR BLACKPORT'S FORWARD MIKE BATESON.

1977-78

AS THE TEAMS WENT OUT AGAIN...

NOW WATCH ENGLAND GO INTO THEIR SHELL AGAIN! RACEY'S SCARED OF *LOSING*, IF YOU ASK ME!

RIGHT! THAT'S THE ONLY REASON HE BROUGHT ON GILES, INSTEAD OF A *FORWARD*...

BUT AS ENGLAND KICKED OFF...

IT'S GILES — PUSHING FORWARD LIKE AN *ATTACKER*!

AND *NOEL BAXTER'S* COMING UP ON HIS LEFT...

WITH YOU, MAC!

...BEAUTIFUL BALL TO BAXTER! BUT ENGLAND HAVE LEFT THEMSELVES WITHOUT ANY COVER!

NEAR POST, NOEL! HIT IT ON THE RUN!

BAXTER'S PASS WAS LOW AND DEADLY... CAUSING SUDDEN, UTTER CONFUSION...

AAUUUFFF!

...THE BALL'S SKIDDED OFF KEPPLE'S LEGS, IT MUST BE A CHANCE...

IT WAS!

...TREVOR FRANCIS! GOOAAAL.

TWO-ONE!

RAAAAY!

THE GIANT SCOREBOARD TOLD ITS OWN, TRIUMPHANT STORY!

FOOTBALL INTERNATIONAL
ENGLAND..................2
HOLLAND.................1
MACDONALD   VALKER
FRANCIS

ENGLAND!

ENGLAAND!

ENGLAND

NOW EVERYONE KNOWS WHAT OUR *TEAM-TALK* WAS ABOUT, ROY! HOLLAND JUST WEREN'T EXPECTING US TO ATTACK THEM FROM THE WORD GO!

ANOTHER LITTLE GAMBLE — AND IT PAID OFF!

THAT'S BEEN THE TROUBLE WITH ENGLAND MANAGERS IN THE PAST, TREVOR. THEY WERE FRIGHTENED TO TAKE A GAMBLE!

WITH THEIR TAILS RIGHT UP, THE ENGLAND PLAYERS REALLY TURNED IT ON!

MACDONALD AGAIN! BUT WHAT A SAVE BY THE DUTCH 'KEEPER!

FIRST TIME CLEARANCE, RAFF — UP THE RIGHT! SEEGRUN IS WAITING FOR IT!

AND, SUDDENLY...

...SEEGRUN'S AWAY! ENGLAND HAVE BEEN LEAVING THEMSELVES WIDE OPEN TO A SUDDEN BREAK — AND *NOW IT'S HAPPENED!*

THERE'S ONLY LOFTY PEAK AND CHARLIE CARTER STANDING BETWEEN HOLLAND ...AND THE *EQUALISER!*

LOFTY PEAK WAS A DEFENDER OF GREAT STATURE, BUT NOW HE LOOKED LIKE A STATUE!

114

SUDDENLY, IT WAS TREVOR FRANCIS TURNED DEFENDER!

116

European Cup – Quarter-final 1st Leg
Rovers 3 Vrayonne Rapide [France] 1
Race (3)
2nd Leg
Vrayonne Rapide 2 Rovers 1
McKay (Pen)
(Rovers win 4-3 on agg.)

Semi-final 1st Leg
Rovers 1 Dorino Dynamos [Italy] 0
Race

Semi-final 2nd Leg
Dorino Dynamos 0 Rovers 0
(Rovers win 1-0 on agg.)

MAY '78 – European Cup Final
Rovers 2 Alkhoven [Holland] 3
Slade, Race

Dutch stars, Seegrun and Valker had gained revenge over Roy Race for England's crushing defeat at Wembley.

SEPTEMBER '78

Controversy reigned when the Sheik of Basran, an oil-rich Middle-Eastern state offered Roy £1 million to take over as his soccer supremo. Although Roy turned him down, the fans were convinced he was about to desert Rovers for a life of luxury. The tension showed in Rovers' early form.

League Cup 2nd Round
Melchester Rovers 0   Norboro 1

League
Melchester Rovers 1   Darlton 2
McKay

Melchester Rovers 1   Portdean 1
Race

By the end of September, Rovers were planted firmly at the foot of the table. Roy, hounded by the Sheik, had scored just once.

DIVISION ONE – BOTTOM FOUR					
	P	W	D	L	Pts
Gatesfield	8	2	2	4	6
Eastgate	8	1	2	5	4
North Vale	7	1	2	4	4
Melchester	7	0	3	4	3

OCTOBER '78

Roy finally found his goal-touch with a double-dose of dynamite against Tynecaster, the second a left-foot strike...

...but despite Roy's re-discovered 'golden touch', Rovers still failed to record their first win of the season – drawing the match 4-4. In Rovers' next game, Roy again struck twice

but failed to secure the much-needed first league win of the season...

Melchester Rovers 3   Burndean 3
Roy (2), Holloway

DECEMBER '78

GALLOWAY REPLACES RACE AS MANAGER

For the first time since his appointment as player-manager, Roy Race has suffered a career set-back. He has relinquished his role as manager of the team in favour of general manager Ben Galloway. Still without a win in the league and decidedly off-form, Roy Race remains submerged in the Basran controversy.
According to Galloway, "This is a positive move for Roy. It will allow him to concentrate on doing what he does best, and that's scoring goals. As soon as we win again, Roy will be back as manager."

JANUARY '79

ROVERS BACK ON SONG

UEFA Cup 3rd Round
Dynamo Zarcov [USSR] v Melchester Rovers

Melchester Rovers are once more focussed on their forte – winning.
In the league, their ambition is to stay out of the relegation zone, after this UEFA Cup performance, Rovers are in the hunt for a European trophy.
In the 3rd Round, Rovers travelled to the USSR with a 4-1, 1st leg win against Dynamo Zarcov under their belts. Not content to sit on their lead, Roy Race scored his third of the tie to win through.

1st leg

Rovers 4   Dynamo Zarcov 1
Race (2),
McKay (Pen.),
Wallace

2nd leg

Dynamo Zarcov 0   Melchester Rovers 1
Race
(Rovers win 5-1 on agg.)

ROY SCORES IN ROVERS' FIRST WIN OF THE SEASON – 4-1 V DYNAMO ZARCOV IN THE UEFA CUP.

A reassured Rovers soon pulled themselves out of the relegation zone...

Melchester Rovers 2   Carford City 0
Race, Gray

Melchester Rovers 1   Walford Rovers 0
Race

FA Cup 3rd Round
Melchester Rovers 8   Kelburn 0
Race (5), Wallace,
Gray, Baxter

Roy scored after just four-seconds of the match, equalling the record for the fastest goal in history. But Rovers lost 1-0 to Carnbrook Town in the next round.

MARCH '79

UEFA Cup Quarter-final 1st Leg
Melchester Rovers v Zaragosa [Spain]

Against Zaragosa, Rovers met right-winger Paco Diaz, Spain's greatest ever player. Diaz and Merv Wallace engaged in a running battle but Diaz triumphed with a pair of goals only cancelled out by Roy. Final score 2-2.

APRIL '79

UEFA Cup Quarter-final 2nd Leg
Zaragosa 0   Melchester Rovers 2
Peak, Gray

MAY '79

Rovers signed Paco Diaz for £700,000. But Diaz would not be eligible to play until the second leg of the final.

UEFA CUP Semi-final
1st Leg
Melchester Rovers 3   Sorbonne (France) 0
Race (2), Eliot

2nd Leg
Sorbonne 0   Melchester Rovers 0
(Rovers win 3-0 on agg.)

To his winger's disgust, Roy dropped Merv Wallace for the first leg of the final against Rassburg of West Germany...

MERVYN WALLACE REGARDED MELCHESTER ROVERS' NEW SIGNING, *PACO DIAZ*, AS A THREAT TO HIS PLACE IN THE SQUAD, AND WHEN *ROY* TOOK DIAZ TO *RASSBURG* FOR THE FIRST LEG OF THE FINAL OF THE *UEFA CUP*, THE MELCHESTER PLAYER-MANAGER SEEMED TO BE INVITING TROUBLE...ESPECIALLY WHEN HE LEFT MERVYN ON THE SUBS' BENCH! THEN, WITH MELCHESTER TRAILING, 1-0, GERRY HOLLOWAY COLLAPSED AFTER TAKING A SHOT AT GOAL...

IS IT BAD, TAFFY?

I'M NOT SURE, ROY! GERRY COULD HAVE TORN THE ACHILLES TENDON, OR JUST PULLED A BUNCH OF FIBRES...

...EITHER WAY I'M NOT TAKING ANY CHANCES! HE'LL HAVE TO GO OFF!

STONE ME! WHAT'S THE BOSS GOING TO DO NOW?

MERVYN WALLACE MAY BE THE NOMINATED SUB, BUT THE LAST THING HE MUST WANT TO DO IS PLAY FOR THE ROVERS!

AYE! HE'S STILL FUMING OVER THE REMARKS THAT PACO MADE AT HALF-TIME!

WE'D BE BETTER OFF PLAYING WITH ONLY TEN MEN!

BUT, TO THE AMAZEMENT OF THE ROVERS...

ROY'S NOT HESITATING! HE'S CALLING MERVYN ON AS SUBSTITUTE!

YOUR USUAL ROLE, MERVYN! ATTACK THEM UP THE LEFT FLANK!

OKAY, OKAY! YOU DON'T HAVE TO TELL ME!

UH—OH! I FEAR THE WORST...

EVEN THE MELCHESTER FANS COULD SENSE MERVYN'S MOOD OF ANGER AND FRUSTRATION...

LOOK AT HIM... HANGING ABOUT OUT ON THE LEFT-WING!

THAT'S WHERE HE'LL STAY FOR THE REST OF THE GAME, IF YOU ASK ME — SULKING!

BUT, SUDDENLY...

HEY, WHAT A RUN!

WALLACE TOOK IT OFF THE GERMANS, JUST AS THEY WERE THINKING OF SETTING UP AN ATTACK!

UUUUH?

JULY '79

ROVERS EXPORT LOFTY

On his return from a summer spent coaching the Basranian national side and setting up the country's first football league, Roy Race announced a deal that would further cement relations between Melchester and Basran.

Roy told the Gazette: "I have been at pains to reject continued offers of permanent employment from the Sheik of Basran. These included the arrival of a brand new Rolls Royce outside my house! I naturally rejected the gift, auctioning it off for charity. As we all feared that this would be the first of a series of unwanted inducements, I was delighted to agree a compromise deal with which both parties are now happy. I am pleased to announce that Lofty Peak, who has come to the end of his contract with Rovers after a long and successful career with the club, will become the full-time national football coach of Basran and will fly-out to take up his post immediately. This is a major career move for Lofty. We wish him well in his job of exporting a little Melchester Magic to our friends in Basran!"

RICH BEYOND THE DREAMS OF GOAL AVERAGE!

AUGUST '79

Having worn out his welcome at a number of clubs, "Superbrat" Vic Guthrie joined Rovers from Westbury Town for a bargain £20,000. He replace Lofty Peak at No.5.

NOVEMBER '79

Hot-tempered Guthrie eventually settled well into the Melchester set-up and Rovers' league form blossomed. Attention then turned to the UEFA Cup. In the first leg in Iceland against part-timers Heklavik, only a Roy Race goal spared Rovers' blushes and they returned home with a fortuitous one-all draw.

In the second leg at Melchester ill-fortune struck the team...

With his team still reeling from the most humiliating moment in their entire history, Roy swore to himself that such a shock would never happen to the mighty Melchester Rovers while he was still wearing its proud colours of red and yellow. His job now was to motivate his devastated players.

To-a-man the players responded to Roy's inspired leadership and Rovers pulled themselves back on the rails of the league title express.

A run of six wins from their next seven league games kept Rovers in the running for the title.

In the fifth round of the F.A. Cup Rovers trailed cross-town rivals Melboro 1-0. But a four-goal burst from Race, Guthrie, Diaz and Gray earned them a sixth round at Fourth Division minnows Chalkford Town. But Roy was again injured before a crucial cup game against much less fancied oposition...

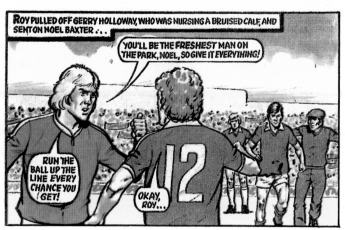

MAY '80

Without any cup concerns, Rovers took the league by storm and set up a rousing finale to an otherwise disappointing season.

LEAGUE TABLE – TOP THREE

	P	W	D	L	Pts
Portdean City	41	25	11	5	61
Tynecaster	42	23	14	5	60
Melchester Rovers	40	24	12	4	60

In their penultimate game at Walford, Rovers were inspired by their player-manager and rammed home five unanswered goals from Race, Dixon, Slade, Gray and Knight.

With Portdean drawing their last game against Carford City, Rovers – with a superior goal difference – needed a single point in their final match to lift the League Championship and to lift the gloom on their dismal cup campaigns...

WHEN THE GOAL-HUNGRY GET TOUGH...

JANUARY '81

Table-propping Rovers had sold Geoff Giles to local rivals Melboro' (breaking a tradition of non-transfers between the clubs).

To replace him Roy signed 35-year-old international, Nat 'Grandad' Gosden on a free transfer from Oldfield. In his debut against Carford City Gosden created the only goal of the game for Roy.

MARCH '81

Rovers bowed out of the European Cup – beaten on away goals by Sweden's Zalmo in the fourth round. But Rovers still had one eye on the F.A. Cup...

AND...

YEESSSSS! IT'S IN!

KELBURN 2, MELCHESTER ROVERS!!

AS THE FINAL WHISTLE SOUNDED, SECONDS LATER...

ROY! I—!

FORGET IT, MERVYN! BEING SORRY WON'T CHANGE THE RESULT...

...WE'RE OUT OF THE F.A. CUP!

NOT EVEN MELCHESTER'S MAGNIFICENT FANS COULD RAISE A SYMPATHETIC CHEER...

I-1... CAN'T BELIEVE IT! THEY JUST THREW THE GAME AWAY!

OLD ROY MUST FEEL LIKE GIVING UP!

THE LAST THING ROY WANTED TO FACE WAS AN AFTER-MATCH INTERVIEW! BUT HE HAD MADE A PROMISE...

WELL, ROY! PROBLEMS ON THE ER— DOMESTIC FRONT... KNOCKED OUT OF ALL THE CUP COMPETITIONS... AND YOU'RE STILL IN DANGER OF RELEGATION! COULD THIS BE MELCHESTER'S BLACKEST SEASON?

THAT DEPENDS ON OUR LAST FEW GAMES, BRIAN...

...REDSTOKE AND CASTLETON ARE ALREADY RELEGATED, SO IT'S BETWEEN US AND NORTH VALE! THEY'RE A POINT CLEAR OF US, WITH TWO GAMES LEFT AND WE'VE GOT THREE! YOU WON'T SEE THE SHAMBLES NEXT SATURDAY THAT YOU SAW TODAY, I CAN GUARANTEE IT!

ROY WAS RIGHT! A WEEK LATER, A LATE GOAL BY ROY GAVE THE ROVERS A NARROW 2-1 VICTORY AT DEANS PARK...

BUT CASTLETON, EVEN THOUGH DOOMED TO THE SECOND DIVISION, WENT DOWN FIGHTING IN ROVERS' SECOND-LAST GAME...

IT'S THERE! CASTLETON HAVE EQUALISED IN THE LAST MINUTE!

AT THE END OF THE GAME, ROY GLANCED UP AT ROVERS' GIANT, ELECTRONIC SCOREBOARD...

GOOD GRIEF...

M/ROVERS 1 CASTLETON 1
NORTH VALE 3 CARFORD 2
OLDFIELD 2 MILBORO 1
REDPOOL 0 BARMOUTH 1

...NORTH VALE BEAT CARFORD IN THEIR LAST GAME! THAT PUTS THEM TWO POINTS CLEAR OF US!

AND IN THE DRESSING-ROOM!

ROY, WE'VE JUST BEEN DOING OUR SUMS—!

SO HAVE I, BLACKIE! IN ORDER TO AVOID RELEGATION ON GOAL DIFFERENCE, WE'VE GOT TO BEAT STAMBRIDGE CITY IN OUR LAST GAME...

...BY FIVE, CLEAR GOALS!

STAMBRIDGE WERE NO PUSH-OVERS

PLAY O

132

1980-81

DECEMBER '81

Gunned down by a mystery assassin, in his office, Roy Race was rushed to Melchester General Hospital, where, after an emergency operation, he was placed on the critical list. In a coma, the situation looked bad for Roy and the whole world waited anxiously for news of his condition. Meanwhile, the entire Melchester police force sprung into action and sent out bulletins looking for five suspects...

Arnie Meckiff – Roy's cousin from Australia, who Roy had threatened to turn in to the police over an illegal land-share scheme in Australia.

Vic Guthrie – Rovers' 'Superbrat', who had been suspended by Roy for disciplinary reasons and faced certain transfer from the club. It was Guthrie, in suspicious circumstances, who had found Roy lying wounded in the office.

Trevor Brinsden – Roy Race's number one fan! But Roy had banned him from all Rovers' home games, due to disturbances on the terraces and outside the ground. Brinsden had sworn to exact revenge on his former idol.

Elton Blake – An actor, who had been sacked from playing the part of Roy Race in an upcoming TV soap series on Melchester Rovers. He too had sworn vengence on Roy.

Arthur Logan – Father of teenager Kenny Logan, who, he believed was coerced by Roy Race into signing for Rovers instead of working in the family estate agency business in Scotland. Another suspect who publicly swore to finish Roy off.

JANUARY '82

With Roy in a coma and Blackie Gray acting as caretaker-manager, Rovers built on their record thirteen game winning start to the season – in the Second Division – and were unbeaten in twenty league games through to Christmas.

The Rovers' board, feeling Roy may never regain consciousness, appointed a new manager – Sir Alf Ramsey.

In his first match in charge, away to Westbury, Sir Alf controversially reinstated (prime suspect) Vic Guthrie to the team – ironically in Roy's hallowed number nine shirt! It took a Merv Wallace goal to earn a point and keep Rovers' record and undefeated league season alive.

FEBRUARY '82

Off the critical list, Roy still showed no signs of coming out of the coma. His wife Penny, and their two children Roy Jr. and Melinda kept a constant vigil at the hospital, hoping for a glimmer of consciousness. The whole of Melchester and Britain were waiting and hoping too.

In his second league game as manager, at home against Keysborough, Sir Alf unveiled his revolutionary, but as yet untried, attacking scheme.

Within minutes of the kick-off, Sir Alf's new system had the visitors transfixed as Rovers' defenders joined in the all-out blitz. Rovers' number four Steve Naylor found himself in acres of space on the left and sent in a low cross trying to get his left-winger in behind the defence...

...HE HAS! VERNON ELIOT!

OHHH! IT'S THERE!

THE ROAR THAT GREETED VERNON'S GOAL WAS STILL ECHOING AROUND THE STADIUM, AS ROVERS WON A CORNER...

VIC GUTHRIE'S GOING UP FOR THE FLAG-KICK!

WATCH HIM, KEYSBORO'.

...HE'LL USE HIS HEIGHT AND STRENGTH TO HUSTLE THE GOALKEEPER!

BUT VIC WAS JUST A DECOY, DESIGNED TO PULL DEFENDERS AWAY FROM PACO DIAZ...

...AND IT'S WORKED! PERFECT CORNER!

GOOOAAAAAAL!

THIS IS FANTASTIC STUFF! LOOK, EVEN THE STADIUM POLICE ARE GOING POTTY!

SO WHAT ARE WE WAITING FOR? ALL TOGETHER NOW...

...LET'S SALUTE THE MAN WHO CAN'T BE HERE TO SHARE IT!

ROY RACE!

ROY RACE!

THE CHANT SPREAD AND SWELLED, ENGULFING THE WHOLE STADIUM IN AN INCREDIBLE WALL OF SOUND...

ROY RACE! ROY RACE!

...EVEN THE PLAYERS PAUSED IN MOMENTARY AWE!

AND THE WAITING DOCTORS HELD THEIR BREATH!

IT'S AS LOUD AS WE CAN GET IT, SIR!

ROY RACE! ROY RACE!

STAND BY, EVERYONE!

ROY RACE! ROY RACE!

COME ON, ROY, COME ON! CAN'T YOU HEAR THEM? THEY'RE SHOUTING FOR YOU!

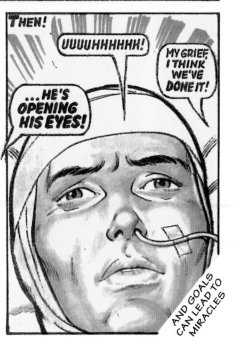

THEN!

UUUUHHHHHH!

MY GRIEF, I THINK WE'VE DONE IT!

...HE'S OPENING HIS EYES!

AND GOALS CAN LEAD TO MIRACLES

THEN...

LADIES AND GENTLEMEN, BOYS AND GIRLS... OUR APOLOGIES TO KEYSBOROUGH FOR INTERRUPTING THE GAME AT THIS POINT... BUT WE HAVE JUST RECEIVED A MESSAGE FROM MELCHESTER GENERAL HOSPITAL...

...AND IT'S THE NEWS WE'VE ALL BEEN WAITING FOR! THE GREATEST NEWS IN THE WORLD! ROY HAS RECOVERED... HE'S OUT OF THE COMA!

WH-WHAT—?

HURRAAAAAAAAAAY!

I RECKON YOU BROUGHT US LUCK, SIR ALF!

ISN'T IT FANTASTIC?

UNBELIEVABLE!

EVEN THE KEYSBOROUGH PLAYERS JOINED IN THE WILD CELEBRATIONS!

WE'RE JUST AS PLEASED AS YOU ARE, BLACKIE!

WAHOOOOOOOO!

AYE! ROY RACE IS SOMETHING SPECIAL TO ALL OF US!

YOU CAN SAY THAT AGAIN! THANKS, LADS!

BUT AS THE GAME RESUMED...

THE 'TRUCE' IS OVER! ROVERS ARE SWAMPING KEYSBOROUGH!

THE NEWS FROM THE HOSPITAL HAS GIVEN THEM SUCH A LIFT, THEY'RE PLAYING LIKE SUPERMEN!

THE CROWD'S THUNDEROUS DEMAND WAS SOON ANSWERED!

GOOOAAAAAL!

JIMMY MADE SURE OF IT, THAT TIME!

WE WANT FOUR! WE WANT FOUR!

AND INEVITABLY...

YESSSSSSS!

WHAT A HEADER FROM BLACKIE GRAY!

THE ROVERS ARE ON THE RAMPAGE!

AT THIS RATE, ROY'S RECOVERY COULD BRING US ANOTHER RECORD...

...THE GREATEST NUMBER OF GOALS SCORED BY ANY TEAM IN A FOOTBALL LEAGUE GAME!

THE FANS WERE RIGHT TO BE OPTIMISTIC

138

1981-82

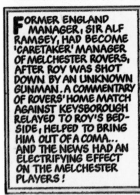

FORMER ENGLAND MANAGER, SIR ALF RAMSEY, HAD BECOME 'CARETAKER' MANAGER OF MELCHESTER ROVERS, AFTER ROY WAS SHOT DOWN BY AN UNKNOWN GUNMAN. A COMMENTARY OF ROVERS' HOME MATCH AGAINST KEYSBOROUGH RELAYED TO ROY'S BED-SIDE, HELPED TO BRING HIM OUT OF A COMA... AND THE NEWS HAD AN ELECTRIFYING EFFECT ON THE MELCHESTER PLAYERS!

GOOOALL!

PACO'S DONE IT FROM THE FREE-KICK!

FIVE-NIL TO THE ROVERS!

AS KEYSBOROUGH'S TACKLING BECAME MORE AND MORE DESPERATE!

AAAAAGH!

THEY ALMOST DRAGGED KENNY LOGAN'S SHIRT OFF!

PENALTY TO MELCHESTER!

DUNCAN McKAY SLAMMED IN THE SPOT—KICK!

NUMBER SIX! YESSSSSS!

WE WANT SEVEN! WE WANT SEVEN!

IN AN ATMOSPHERE OF UTTER PANDEMONIUM, MERVYN WALLACE OBLIGED THE MELCHESTER FANS!

HURAAAAAY!

SEVEN-NIL! I FEEL ALMOST SORRY FOR KEYSBOROUGH!

I WONDER IF ROY IS LISTENING TO THIS?

SURE ENOUGH, AT MELCHESTER GENERAL HOSPITAL...

'...BLACKIE GRAY... AND IT'S THERE! SEVEN-NIL! I... I MEAN, EIGHT! GOOD GRIEF, I'M BEGINNING TO LOSE COUNT!'

IT SOUNDS AS IF THE ROVERS MIGHT BE GETTING ON TOP, ROY!

AYE...

:..WHAT'S... WHAT'S THE RECORD FOR THE...MOST GOALS SCORED BY... ONE TEAM IN A...FOOTBALL LEAGUE GAME, PENNY?

ROY RACE! YOU'VE BEEN UNCONSCIOUS FOR SEVEN WEEKS AND ALL YOU CAN THINK ABOUT IS FOOTBALL!

BUT SOMEONE SOON CAME UP WITH THE ANSWER...

A CHAP IN THE NEXT WARD IS A FOOTBALL FANATIC ROY! HE SAYS IT'S THIRTEEN GOALS... BY NEWCASTLE, STOCKPORT AND TRANMERE!

SO...ROVERS NEED ANOTHER... SIX TO...BREAK THE RECORD...

NEXT UP IT WAS BLACKIE GRAY'S TURN...

1981-82

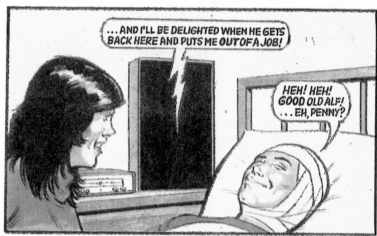

FEBRUARY '82

Following Rovers' record-breaking fourteen-nil win, Roy soon made a full recovery and was released from hospital – although the identity of his assailant, despite exhaustive police investigations, remained a mystery.

MARCH '82

Roy was still not sufficiently recovered to resume his managerial duties and Rovers remained under Sir Alf's capable stewardship. Through his solid command, Rovers continued their incredible season notching up a record-breaking 34 games undefeated in the league.

APRIL '82

With Roy now back at work, but still not match fit, Sir Alf, his role completed, stood down as manager and handed the team back over to Roy, who now faced the enormous challenge of continuing Sir Alf's unbeaten run.

But Roy's return to the big time was far from a fairytale homecoming. In his first game back as manager, Rovers quickly found themselves 3-0 down to Darlton. Although Roy's men were determined to give their boss a welcome-back-victory – launching a spirited fightback with goals from Gray, McKay and Logan – Rovers lost their first league game of the season by the odd goal in seven.

MAY '82

Rovers soon put the Darlton loss behind them as the Second Division championship remained a mere formality. Now fully fit and restless to resume playing, Roy made his long-awaited comeback against Hunterford. He was immediately back on form, scoring Rovers' first two goals in the 3-0 win. Roy took himself off at half-time and went to Melchester police station – where he gave evidence that led to the arrest of actor Elton Blake – for attempted murder.

In the last league game of the season at Rotherton, Rovers, confirmed as Second Division, signed off in style with a 4-1 win and Roy Race ended a traumatic season with a hat-trick!

BRING ME THE HEAD OF ROY RACE

JULY '82

On 10th July Roy's wife Penny gave birth to a daughter – a new sister for twins Roy jnr. and Mel. As they discussed a name for their baby, the recent Royal wedding of Prince Charles and Lady Diana gave them an idea.

JULY '82

Rovers were preparing for their first season back in Division 1, but the squad was not at full strength. Charlie Carter and Merv Wallace were nursing injuries which kept them well out of contention. But worst of all, Vernon Eliot had been trampled on in a pitch invasion at a pre-season cricket match. Vernon's leg injury put an end to his playing career.

AUGUST '82

Chairman Sam Barlow offered Roy £2 million to spend on the transfer market. But Roy decided not to enter the market-place. He believed that Melchester's wealth greatly inflated the asking price for players. "With three senior and youth teams, we must be able to promote talent from within", he told Mr Barlow.

For Rovers' first match of the season Roy was forced to bring in Nat 'Grandad' Gosden in midfield and rooky Walter Williams in goal.

AUGUST '82

Melchester Rovers 1   Holverton 4
Race

After one of Rovers' heaviest league defeats at the start of the season, Roy brought goal-keeper Tubby Morton out of retirement to play against old rivals Carford City.

Melchester Rovers 2   Carford City 1
Gray, Race

Out-of-form Tubby was slow and bewildered at the start of the game: With each passing minute Rovers' rotund goalie came nearer to passing-out. "You've got the stamina of a horse and the heart of a lion", Roy told him, but an exhausted Tubby only just survived!

NOVEMBER '82

Still beset by injuries, Rovers soldiered on in the league, relying on their elder statesmen.

The fans and the board of directors were becoming impatient and increasingly embarrassed about their threadbare team. Roy was also feeling the pressures at home. In the Race family the score was adults 2 v kids 3 and the strain of coping with squabbling toddlers and a demanding baby was wearing Roy out. Under pressure, deprived of sleep, he was tired at work and at home and became prickly when his decisions were questioned. Roy's unhappiness with his lot was deepening.

DECEMBER '82

Former winger Vernon Eliot was appointed assistant manager of Rovers' youth team.

DECEMBER '82

Meanwhile, the Rovers board was instigating an ambitious plan to transform Mel Park into the most modern stadium in the country.

Rovers' home would be Britain's first all-seater. When asked for his opinion at a meeting called to discuss the plans, Roy was found fast asleep! However, awoken with a start, the shattered manager managed to point out that the proposed leisure centre would block fans' access to the River Stand...back to the drawing board!

DECEMBER '82

Melchester Rovers 2   Portdean 1
Race, Logan

Melchester Rovers 0   Tynecaster 1
(Match abandoned)

In this snow-affected game, Rovers were on the brink of a humiliating league defeat when it was called-off due to the impossible conditions. The snow had deepened and the pitch froze over as the temperature plummeted, but this was nothing compared to the icy reception Roy received from the fans. The physical well-being of Tubby Morton was becoming a cause for concern, but still he soldiered on, as Rovers remained undefeated with him in goal. Roy stayed faithful to an ailing Tubby, but his was the minority view.

JANUARY '83

Goalkeeper Charlie 'The Cat' Carter was fit and ready to return, but Roy refused to replace Tubby in goal for Rovers' next match against Walford and Charlie threatened to resign. The heat on Roy was increasing.

FEBRUARY '83

Melchester Rovers 4   Walford Rovers 0
Race (4)

A group of hardline fans led by Trevor Brinsden protested outside Roy's house chanting, 'Bring back The Cat or resign.' Tubby Morton bowed out of goalkeeping to concentrate on running his sports shop. This left the field open for Charlie Carter to return to the first team after injury.

FEBRUARY '83

RAWSON COURTS ROY RACE

Harvey Rawson, the new chairman of Walford Rovers, has offered Roy Race a £3,000 a week salary plus £5 million spending money if he leaves Melchester Rovers and joins Division One Walford as player-manager.

Rawson promises that he has the money to build the London side into Europe's finest football team and he believes only one man can help him achieve his goal. That man is Roy Race. Rawson's offer is being treated with contempt by all those connected with Rovers, directors and fans alike. Roy has rejected many such inducements in his time and has always maintained that he would never quit Melchester, no matter what the price. Roy may be going through a hard time just now, but the fans are sure that his heart will always remain with Melchester Rovers.

MARCH '83

Roy felt that he was being taken for granted at Rovers and this angered him. Players, fans, even Roy's wife, Penny refused to take the Walford offer seriously. To make matters worse, his decisions were being questioned by the board and players alike. Roy's reaction – fuelled by his hurt pride – was to think seriously about Rawson's offer.

BY APRIL ROY HAD FOUND THE SOLUTION TO HIS PROBLEMS. THE 'ROCKET' WAS ABOUT TO ENTER A NEW ORBIT.

THE TWO TEAMS WERE MATCHED AT 2-2. ROVERS HAD TWICE BEEN TRAILING TO LOWLY REDSTOKE, WITH GOALS FROM ROY RACE AND PACO DIAZ MANAGING TO KEEP THEM IN THE GAME. BUT GOALKEEPER CHARLIE 'THE CAT' CARTER HAD RECEIVED A KNOCK IN A GOALMOUTH INCIDENT AND RATHER THAN RISK RECURRENCE OF HIS COLLAR BONE INJURY, ROY HAD CONTROVERSIALLY TAKEN CARTER OFF AND TAKEN HIS PLACE IN GOAL! MINUTES LATER, OUT OF THE REFEREE'S SIGHT, ROY LAY CONCUSSED AFTER A BRAVE SAVE.

MANY FANS WERE EQUALLY CYNICAL ABOUT ROVERS' VICTORY...

LUCKIEST THREE POINTS THEY'LL EVER GET!

YOU WERE ROBBED, REDSTOKE!

I STILL DON'T UNDER-STAND WHY ROY PULLED OFF CHARLIE CARTER!

TAFFY, HOW IS CHARLIE?

YOU NEEDN'T HAVE WORRIED, ROY! THERE WAS NO DAMAGE TO HIS COLLAR-BONE! BUT CHARLIE WAS A BIT UPSET AND HE, ER...

HE WALKED OUT IN DISGUST... AND I DON'T BLAME HIM! ROY, THAT WAS NO WAY TO TREAT A GOALKEEPER OF CARTER'S REPUTATION!

NOW, WAIT A MINUTE, SAM...

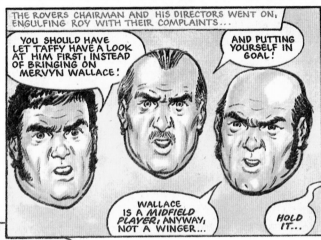

THE ROVERS CHAIRMAN AND HIS DIRECTORS WENT ON, ENGULFING ROY WITH THEIR COMPLAINTS...

YOU SHOULD HAVE LET TAFFY HAVE A LOOK AT HIM FIRST, INSTEAD OF BRINGING ON MERVYN WALLACE!

AND PUTTING YOURSELF IN GOAL!

WALLACE IS A MIDFIELD PLAYER, ANYWAY, NOT A WINGER...

HOLD IT...

...HOLD IIIIIIT! GOOD GRIEF, THE WAY YOU'RE GOING ON, ANYONE WOULD THINK THAT WE HAD LOST THE GAME! I DID WHAT I THOUGHT BEST FOR CHARLIE AND THE TEAM...

...SUPPOSE CHARLIE HAD DAMAGED HIS COLLAR-BONE? IF I'D ALLOWED HIM TO PLAY ON, HE MIGHT HAVE BROKEN IT AGAIN! AND YOU SEEM TO FORGET THAT TWO OF OUR GOALS WERE SET UP BY MERVYN WALLACE...

...BUT IF YOU DON'T LIKE IT, RUN THE TEAM YOUR-SELF! EVERYONE SEEMS TO WANT TO BE MANAGER, THESE DAYS!

ROY! WHERE ARE YOU GOING?

SHAKING WITH FURY AND INDIGNATION, ROY STORMED INTO HIS OFFICE AND LOCKED THE DOOR BEHIND HIM!

ROY... ROY!

THAT DOES IT! THEY'VE TRIED TO TELL ME HOW TO RUN THE TEAM ONCE TOO OFTEN...

ROY RACE
PLAYER MAN

...IT'S TIME I MADE THAT TELEPHONE CALL TO THE CHAIRMAN OF WALFORD ROVERS!

ROY ACCEPTED RAWSON'S OFFER AND BECAME ROY OF ANOTHER ROVERS – WALFORD ROVERS. HIS DEBUT WAS AGAINST DEANS PARK...

1982-83

WALFORD ROVERS 0   DEANS PARK 0

1982-83

20 MINUTES IN, DEANS PARK LED 1-0. ROY HAD TO PROVE HE COULD SCORE FOR A TEAM OTHER THAN MELCHESTER.

SOON AFTER THE RESTART, AS DEANS PARK WERE AWARDED A THROW-IN...

WATCH RACE, MARTIN!

AWW FORGET HIM! HE'S STILL DREAMING ABOUT THE ROVERS!

HEY—!

LOOK AT THIS!

ROY'S EXPLODING THROUGH THEIR DEFENCE...

...AND THERE'S THE 'ROCKET'!

GOOOOAAAAL!

WHAT A SHOT!

WE WONDERED WHEN YOU WERE GOING TO GET STARTED, RACEY!

BETTER LATE THAN NEVER, EH? NOW LET'S SHOW THESE PEOPLE THAT WALFORD AREN'T A ONE-MAN TEAM!

AS THE WALFORD PLAYERS PICKED THEMSELVES UP AND TOOK AN IRON GRIP ON THE GAME...

TWO-ONE! THAT'S BETTER, WALFORD!

HAVEN'T SEEN THEM PLAY SO POSITIVELY IN YEARS!

MOMENTS LATER...

ROY AGAIN!

LOVELY CROSS, MIKE!

WAHOOOO! THAT'S THE WAY TO CONVERT HALF-CHANCES!

AT HALF-TIME...

ROY! I...I...

IT'S ALL RIGHT, HARVEY, I KNOW WHAT YOU'RE GOING TO SAY...SOMETHING ABOUT 'COMMITMENT' ...AND 'LOYALTY'...

WELL, RIGHT NOW, MY LOYALTIES ARE WITH WALFORD! YOU BROUGHT ME HERE TO DO A JOB AND I'M GOING TO DO IT TO THE BEST OF MY ABILITY; NO MATTER HOW MUCH I'M MISSING THE ROVERS...

...WHICH REMINDS ME, I'VE GOT TO FIND OUT HOW THEY'RE GETTING ON AGAINST TYNECASTER! WHERE'S THE NEAREST TELEPHONE?

WALFORD ROVERS 2   DEANS PARK 1

ROY FOUND OUT THAT MELCHESTER WERE TRAILING 1-0. BUT HE KNEW HE HAD TO FORGET THEIR PLIGHT AND GIVE HIS ALL FOR WALFORD ROVERS. IN THE SECOND HALF...

NO-ONE COULD HAVE PLAYED HARDER FOR WALFORD, OR COVERED MORE GROUND THAN ROY!

HUH?

COME ON, BELLAMY... MOVE! YOU'RE SUPPOSED TO BE TACKLING HIM, NOT ADMIRING HIS FOOTWORK!

AND...

GREAT BALL! AND JOHNSON WAS WAITING FOR IT, THIS TIME!

THEY'RE BEGINNING TO GET THE HANG OF THE 'MELCHESTER' STYLE...

ROY FOLLOWED UP WITH A SPEED THAT STUNNED THE DEANS PARK DEFENCE...

HE'S RIGHT ON THE SPOT FOR THE CROSS!

THIS IS FOR THE ROVERS! THE 'ROVERS' I'M PLAYING FOR NOW...

...AND THE 'ROVERS' I LEFT BEHIND!

YESSSSSS!

LATE IN THE GAME, ROY PUT THE SEAL ON A MAGNIFICENT DISPLAY...

WHAT A CRACKER! FIVE-ONE!

ROY COULDN'T HAVE PLAYED ANY BETTER FOR MELCHESTER!

AT FULL-TIME...

ROY RACE! ROY RACE! ROY RAAACE!

NO-ONE COULD HAVE ANY DOUBTS ABOUT HIS DEDICATION NOW!

ROY'S WORTH EVERY PENNY THAT IT COST TO BRING HIM HERE!

THE WALFORD DIRECTORS WERE IN FULL AGREEMENT...

WHAT A PLAYER! WHAT A MAN!

IN HIS VERY FIRST MATCH, HE'S MADE HIMSELF THE IDOL OF WALFORD!

THAT'S RIGHT! WITH THIS CLUB, HE COULD WIN EVERY HONOUR IN THE GAME, ALL OVER AGAIN...

...BUT THE PROSPECT DOESN'T SEEM TO EXCITE HIM VERY MUCH, DOES IT?

WALFORD ROVER 5   DEANS PARK 1
MELCHESTER ROVERS 1   TYNECASTER 2

1982-83

ANOTHER GOLD BRICK IN THE WALFORD LINE-UP

JULY '83

Roy, now player-manager of Walford Rovers was living alone in Walford, separated from wife Penny and his three children. Penny had refused to move from Melchester and in anger took the children to Crete on holiday. Roy had lost Melchester Rovers and was now in danger of losing his family as well. He was also receiving hate mail from Melchester fans who felt betrayed by his professional loyalty to Walford Rovers.

JULY '83

Blackie Gray was appointed player-manager of Melchester Rovers.

JULY '83

RACE RUNS THE GAUNTLET

Vernon Eliot Benefit Match
Melchester Rovers 0   Roy Race Int. XI 3
Hunt, Morgan, Bird

Roy has faced the music at Melchester. He ran the gauntlet of angry former colleagues and fans by returning to Mel Park for this emotional match and triumphed. Race received a hostile reception, but football is a great leveller and soon all animosity turned to respect for Roy's skills and vision which have been much missed at Rovers. Although his team won 3-0, Roy couldn't, or wouldn't, score against his beloved Rovers.

After the game young Rovers' fans unrolled a giant petition calling for his return. Roy went immediately to see the Melchester directors to bury the hatchet. But chairman Sam Barlow was in no mood for reconciliation.

AUGUST '83

Blackie Gray brought Rob 'Superkid' Richards into Rovers' first team, from the youth squad. Richards, with his uncanny resemblance to Roy Race, was hailed as the new Roy of the Rovers.

AUGUST '83

Paco Diaz, Rovers' legendary Spanish superstar winger, returned to Real Varagosa.
Rumours flew as newspapers carried photographs of Roy – who was still separated from Penny – escorting a gorgeous blonde to a Walford supporters club dance. But Roy was innocent, the mysterious lady was Sandie Lewis, his secretary.

SANDIE LEWIS

AUGUST '83

Melchester Rovers   1   Tynecaster 2
Richards

Walford Rovers 4   North Vale 0
Race (3), Shields

SEPTEMBER '83

Penny Race flew back from Crete and straight into the Sandie Lewis controversy. She prolonged her separation from Roy. The crisis engulfed Roy, and told on the pitch.

Redstoke 3   Walford Rovers 0

OCTOBER '83

Ever the professional, Roy knew he must put his personal problems behind him...

Walford Rovers 6   Melboro 1
Race (4), Shields,
Wright

Without Roy, disaster struck Melchester in the First Round of the Milk Cup.

Sefton Town (Div 4) 2   Melchester Rovers 1
Richards

NOVEMBER '83

Despite creating plenty of opportunities, Roy couldn't score against Melchester Rovers.

Melchester Rovers 1   Walford Rovers 2
Gorman, Bellamy

NOVEMBER '83

Losing to Roy Race's Walford Rovers was the ultimate humiliation for Sam Barlow. After an altercation with Blackie Gray, who stood up to the irate chairman, Barlow quit Rovers.

NOVEMBER '83

After Barlow's exit, Walford chairman Harvey Rawson, aware that Roy's loyalty lay with Melchester, released Roy from his contract.
Reunited at last with Penny, who now believed he was to blame for the Sandie Lewis incident. Roy moved back to Melchester. In his first game, the prodigal son signalled his return by displaying his priceless, match-winning gifts.

Melchester Rovers 1   Portdean 0
Race

JANUARY '84

Neville Jones, signed from Melton, made his first team debut in the third-round of the FA Cup.

Melchester Rovers 2   Wokington Town 1
Race, Jones

FEBRUARY '84

FA Cup 4th Round
Portdean 2   Melchester Rovers 5
Gray, Guthrie, Race,
Ritchie, Slade

FA Cup 5th Round
Melchester Rovers 3   Swinfield (Div.4) 0
Logan, Gray, Richards

MARCH '84

FA Cup Quarter-final
Carford City 0   Melchester Rovers 6
Slade, Jones, Baxter,
Gray, Richards, Race

APRIL '84

FA Cup Semi-final
Melchester Rovers 5   Weston Villa 1
Race (4), Richards

Rovers' opponents in the final were Walford!

INJURIES FORCED ROVERS TO FIELD A 'PATCH-WORK' TEAM, WITH YOUNGSTERS WALTER WILLIAMS IN GOAL AND ERROL BRIDGER IN DEFENCE. FROM THE KICK-OFF WALFORD PUT ROVERS' YOUNG DEFENCE UNDER PRESSURE.

THE CROSS WAS INCH-PERFECT...

GET *IN* THERE!

YOUNG WALTER WILLIAAMS, ANOTHER REPLACEMENT, COULD ONLY PALM THE BALL AGAINST THE CROSS-BAR...

OOOOOGH!

IT'S REBOUNDED!

BELLAMY WAS UP OFF THE GROUND IN A FLASH!

YESSSSSS!

MELCHESTER ROVERS 0, WALFORD ROVERS 1!

AND THERE'S MORE TO COME, MELCHESTER! YOU'RE *RUBBISH!* YOU'VE ONLY GOT HALF A TEAM!

GOOD OLD JOE!

THE CUP'S AS GOOD AS OURS!

ER... SORRY, ROY!

MY FAULT! I... SHOULD HAVE STOPPED IT!

I'LL TELL YOU ONE THING THAT YOU TWO CAN *STOP...*

...AND THAT'S *APOLOGISING!* IT'S NOT GOING TO GET US BACK INTO THIS GAME! SO LET'S FORGET IT AND START AGAIN!

ROY, DON'T FORGET THAT ERROL IS UP AGAINST WALFORD'S BEST STRIKER! MAYBE WE OUGHT TO SWITCH THE KID UNTIL HE SETTLES DOWN!

WE'LL SEE, BLACKIE, IF OUR FANS START TO BARRACK HIM, I-!

TO CHEERS FROM THE MELCHESTER FANS, ROVERS MOUNTED A FIGHT BACK

1983-84

BUT WALFORD GAINED POSSESSION AND MOUNTED A CONCERTED ASSAULT ON THE ROVERS' GOAL, TESTING THE BRAVERY OF YOUNG GOALKEEPER WALTER WILLIAMS TO THE LIMIT.

WALTER COULD DO LITTLE MORE THAN THROW HIMSELF INTO THE PATH OF THE BALL!

AAAUUNNNF!

AND SOMEHOW...

IT'S REBOUNDED OVER THE BAR... OFF HIS SHOULDER!

OOOHHH, THE LUCKY LITTLE...

A DERISIVE CHANT ROSE FROM THE WALFORD FANS!

LUCKY, LUCKY, LUCKY, LUCKY, MELCHESTER!

THEY'RE RIGHT, WALTER! BUT THE GREATEST PLAYERS IN THE WORLD NEED A SLICE OF GOOD FORTUNE ALONG THE WAY...

...AND YOU'VE JUST HAD YOURS! A BIG SLICE! FOR GOODNESS SAKE, DON'T WASTE IT!

I...I'LL TRY NOT TO, ROY.

AS THE CORNER WAS TAKEN...

AN OUT-SWINGER! GO ON, JOE BELLAMY... KNOCK IT IN!

THAT'S JOE'S!

WILLIAMS'LL NEED MORE THAN LUCK, THIS TIME!

BUT!

THAT'S WALTER WILLIAMS'!

UUUH?

GREAT CATCH!

AND A GREAT THROW TO TREVOR CASSIDY!

THAT LET-OFF SEEMS TO HAVE TRANSFORMED THE KID!

TREVOR CASSIDY WAS ANOTHER REPLACEMENT... AN EXPERIENCED PROFESSIONAL, AND THE ELECTRIC, WEMBLEY ATMOSPHERE HELD NO FEARS FOR HIM...

LOOK AT HIM HOLDING THE BALL... ALLOWING THE OTHER MELCHESTER PLAYERS TO RUN INTO GOOD POSITIONS!

GET ON HIM, YOU STUPID—!

HE'S DRAWN JOE BELLAMY... AND FED THE BALL TO MERVYN WALLACE!

ROY YELLED THROUGH THE UPROAR!

GO FOR IT, MERVYN! RUN AT THE DEFENCE!

AND THERE HE GOES! PEOPLE TEND TO FORGET THAT MERVYN WALLACE CAME TO MELCHESTER AS A *FAST, RAIDING WINGER*...

...WHO LOVES TO TAKE ON PLAYERS AND *BEAT* THEM.

LIKE *THAT*...

...AND *THAT!*

HE'S NEARLY THERE! GO ON, MERVYN, GO ON!

HIT IT, MERV!

A DESPERATE, LATE TACKLE SENT MERVYN WALLACE SPRAWLING!

AAAAAGH!

FOUL, REF.. FOUL!

BUT THE REFEREE PENALISED WALFORD BY ALLOWING PLAY TO CONTINUE...

ROY—!

AND IT'S THERE... 'THE ROCKET'!

YESSSSSSSS!

MELCHESTER ROVERS 1, WALFORD 1!

WALFORD'S FIRST SHOT AFTER HALF-TIME HIT THE POST, IT WAS ANYONE'S BALL...

UUNNF!

BRIDGER'S SNAPPED UP THE REBOUND!

ERROL BRIDGER WAS ONE OF FIVE MEL-CHESTER REPLACEMENTS FOR THE MOST SENSATIONAL CUP FINAL IN HISTORY!

INFIELD TO ROY! GREAT PASS!

THE WALFORD PLAYERS ARE WRONG-FOOTED!

NOT ALL OF THEM, RACEY!

BELLAMY! STILL TALKING ...COMPETING... FIGHTING TO THE LAST!

THE TWO GREAT RIVALS REFUSED TO YIELD AN INCH!

NNNNNF!

GUH!

THE BALL'S LOOSE ...AND IT'S NEARLY ALL OVER! THEY'LL HAVE TO PLAY EXTRA-TIME!

BUT!

NEVILLE JONES! HE'S GONE FOR IT!

IN! ...AND IT'S IN OFF THE CROSSBAR!

YESSSSSSSS!

COME ON, WALFORD, PICK YOURSELVES UP! JUST ONE GOAL AND WE'RE BACK IN IT! THEY CAN'T HAVE ALL THE LUCK!

WE'RE WITH YOU, JOE!

ONE LAST EFFORT, LADS!

A PATCH-WORK ROVERS' SIDE HAD LIFTED THE CUP – WILLIAMS, BRIDGER, GUTHRIE, CASSIDY, NAYLOR, SLADE, RICHARDS, WALLACE, GRAY, RACE AND JONES. EVEN AS ROY CELEBRATED THEIR CUP WIN, HE WAS THINKING OF ROVERS' FUTURE. HE SIGNED MIDFIELDER CARL 'THE HUNTER' HUNT FROM CARFORD CITY.

1983-84

ROY SIGNS UP FOR NATIONAL SERVICE!

"I'M A VERY PRIVILEGED CRICKETER... PRIVILEGED TO BE ASSOCIATED WITH A FOOTBALL CLUB THAT I CONSIDER TO BE ONE OF THE BEST IN BRITAIN!"

AUGUST '84

Test cricketer Geoffrey Boycott was appointed chairman of Melchester Rovers.

DECEMBER '84

Injury-plagued Rovers were floundering in the league. Goalkeeper Andy 'Streaky' Styles moved up into the first team. He gained his nickname through his brilliant but erratic goalkeeping.

JANUARY '85

FA Cup 3rd Round
Ramsden Town 1   Melchester Rovers 0

FEBRUARY '85

Roy, Neville Jones and Carl Hunt were selected to play for England against France at Wembley. Named captain, Roy was nursing an ankle injury and in playing risked missing Rovers' next game.

AGAINST FRANCE ROY FACED OLD ADVERSARY, FRENCH COACH, CARLOS VILLAR. AS A PLAYER VILLAR HAD NEARLY ENDED ROY'S CAREER WITH A CYNICAL TACKLE IN THE EUROPEAN CUP. FOR THE INTERNATIONAL HE HAD GIVEN HIS DEFENDERS, GRIMOND AND LORIAN ORDERS TO TAKE ROY OUT IN A SIMILAR MANNER.
IN A GOAL-LESS FIRST-HALF ROY HAD BEEN HIT HARD. BUT HE KNEW HE WOULD HAVE TO TAKE EVEN MORE PUNISHMENT TO GIVE HIS FORWARDS GREATER FREEDOM. IT WAS A GAMBLE THAT COULD END IN DISASTER FOR ROVERS' FUTURE. FROM THE RE-START A FEARLESS ROY POUNCED ON A LOOSE PASS...

ENGLAND 1, FRANCE 0.

ENGLAND 1 FRANCE 1
RACE

Roy's worst nightmare had come true, he was immediately ruled out of Rovers' vital European Cup-Winners' Cup Quarter-final home leg against Belgium side Bokeren. But Roy's gamble with his own fitness had paid off because Rovers performed well without him and Styles proved his international ability by saving a penalty.

1st Leg
Melchester Rovers 4   Bokeren 0
Baxter, Hunter,
Butler, Logan

2nd Leg
Roy was back for the away leg.

Bokeren 0   Melchester Rovers 1
        Race
(Rovers win 5-0 on agg.)

MARCH '85

Rovers' league form was mixed.

Melchester Rovers 4   Oldfield 0
Race 2, Richards 2

Melchester Rovers 1   Portdean 3
Hunt

APRIL '85

But in Europe, in the Cup-Winners' Cup, they were unstoppable.

European Cup-Winners' Cup
Semi-final 1st Leg
Stahlberg [W.Ger.] 0   Rovers 5
        Jones, Hunt (2)
        Race (2)

APRIL '85

Nat 'Grandad' Gosden was appointed youth team manager.

MAY '85

European Cup-Winners' Cup
Semi-final 2nd leg
Melchester Rovers 2   Stahlberg 0
Richards, Hunt

(Rovers win 7-0 on agg.)

MAY '85

European Cup-Winners' Cup Final
Rovers v Real Santana [Spain]

EUROPEAN CUP-WINNERS' CUP FINAL MELCHESTER ROVERS V REAL SANTANA [SPAIN]

The first-half had been an ugly affair, under Carlos Villar, Real Santana were a dirty side. In the semi-final against Glenmore, Perez had broken Duncan McKay's brother's leg. Irate Glenmore fans had travelled to Belgium to support Rovers. Caught up in the tension of this 'grudge match' Rovers had frozen and allowed Real to take a commanding lead. First, a hesitant Duncan McKay had pulled out of an easy tackle to concede a simple goal. Next, McKay fouled Perez just outside the edge of Rovers' penalty area, but the referee awarded a penalty which Real converted. In the second half, goals from Roy and Neville Jones levelled it at 2-2. Coach Villar's aim was to take out Roy and he unleashed towering defender, Basora who had laid out three men in the Semi-final.

AS THE GAME WORE ON, AND REAL CONCENTRATED ON PRESERVING THEIR 2-1 LEAD, MARK BUTLER, THE ROVERS' BALL-PLAYING DEFENDER, BEGAN TO PUSH FORWARD . . .

HE'S RELEASED ROY! *BRILLIANT* BALL!

GO ON, RACEY!

ROY, *WATCH IT!* MAN ON!

BASORA!

AAAAAAGH!

. . . BUT ROY HAD MANAGED TO KNOCK THE BALL INSIDE . . .

. . . STRAIGHT TO THE FEET OF NEVILLE JONES. AND . . .

YESSSSSSS!

THE *EQUALISER!* MELCHESTER 2, REAL SANTANA 2!

OOOOOOOHHH!

BUT ROY'S STILL DOWN! BASORA'S STUDS RAKED THE BACK OF HIS LEFT LEG . . .

. . . AND THERE'S THE WHISTLE TO END *NINETY MINUTES!* ROVERS WILL HAVE TO PLAY EXTRA-TIME *WITHOUT* THEIR BEST PLAYER!

REAL *MUST* BE FAVOURITES NOW!

IT LOOKED LIKE CARLOS VILLAR'S DIRTY TACTICS HAD FINALLY PAID OFF AS ROVERS' MATCH-WINNING GENIUS LAY WRITHING IN AGONY. VILE VILLAR THOUGHT HE HAD ACHIEVED WHAT HE HAD FAILED TO DO AS COACH OF THE FRENCH SIDE. HE HAD OVERCOME PURE SOCCER GENIUS BY EMPLOYING METHODS WHICH FURTHER SOILED HIS ALREADY TARNISHED REPUTATION IN INTERNATIONAL FOOTBALL.

1984-85

AS SUBSTITUTE KENNY LOGAN PREPARED TO TAKE ROY'S PLACE...

HOLD IT, KENNY! THE INJURY MAY NOT BE AS BAD AS EVERYONE THINKS!

THANKS TO THE *PRECAUTIONS* THAT WE TOOK WITH EVERY PLAYER...

...A LAYER OF *SURGICAL BANDAGE*, STRAPPED AROUND THEIR LEGS, UNDER THEIR STOCKINGS! IT'S SAVED ROY FROM THE WORST EFFECTS OF BASORA'S STUDS!

MEANWHILE, AS EXTRA-TIME BEGAN, THE SPANIARDS WERE TRYING TO TAKE ADVANTAGE OF ROY'S ABSENCE...

OHHHHH, *BRILLIANT* MOVE!

IT EVEN WRONG-FOOTED ANDY STYLES!

JUST WIDE!

ROVERS ARE *ASKING* FOR TROUBLE, PLAYING ON WITH ONLY TEN MEN!

IF ROY'S CROCKED, WHY DOESN'T HE SEND ON THE *SUB?*

MAYBE THEY'RE TRYING TO PATCH HIM UP!

CARLOS VILLAR SNEERED AS HE HEARD THE CRIES OF THE ROVERS FANS!

YOU HAVE SEEN THE LAST OF YOUR HERO, GENTLEMEN... THE SO-CALLED 'KING' OF MELCHESTER! VILLAR HAS SEEN TO THAT, YET AGAIN!

THEN, AS REAL WON A THROW-IN...

LOOK, IT'S *ROY*... SIGNALLING TO THE REF!

HE WANTS TO COME BACK *ON!*

THE MERE SIGHT OF ROY HAD AN ELECTRIFYING EFFECT ON THE ROVERS!

RACEY'S *BACK*...HE'S *OKAY!*

THAT'S *GREAT*... *FANTASTIC!*

WE'LL SORT THEM OUT NOW, LADS!

1984-85

WITH ROY BACK ON, A PENALTY GAVE MCKAY THE CHANCE FOR REVENGE — BUT HE MISSED. MEANWHILE, VILLAR RECEIVED A RED CARD FOR ATTACKING THE REFEREE.

ALMOST IMMEDIATELY, THE REFEREE'S WHISTLE ENDED THE FIRST PERIOD OF EXTRA-TIME!

OCH, I....I'M SORRY, LADS... I TRIED TOO HARD!

IN THE CRAZY ATMOSPHERE OF THIS GAME, I'M NOT SURPRISED. FORGET IT!

WE'VE STILL FIFTEEN MINUTES TO WRAP IT UP, DUNCAN!

THEN...

HEY, ROY! I LIKE A WORD WITH YOU!

MAKE IT QUICK, BASORA... AND MAKE IT POSITIVE! YOUR MANAGER HAS COME UP WITH ENOUGH DIRTY TRICKS TO LAST YOU LOT THE WHOLE OF NEXT SEASON!

I KNOW... WE NOT PROUD OF IT! WE ONLY OURSELVES TO PLAY FOR NOW... THE HONOUR OF REAL!

NOT FORGETTING THOSE FANS UP THERE! ENGLISH, SPANISH, SCOTS! A LOT OF THEM BEHAVE ACCORDING TO THE STANDARDS THAT WE SET ON THE PITCH...

...SO LET'S GIVE THEM SOMETHING GOOD TO REMEMBER, IN THE FIFTEEN MINUTES WE'VE GOT LEFT!

THAT GOES FOR REAL!

FOR THE FIRST TIME, THE FINAL BECAME A GAME OF SKILL, EXCITEMENT, AND SHEER, WHOLEHEARTED ENDEAVOUR!

BUT FIFTEEN MINUTES LATER...

IT'S ALL OVER! THE GAME'S ENDED IN STALE-MATE!

THEY'LL HAVE TO SETTLE IT WITH SPOT-KICKS NOW!

A PENALTY SHOOT-OUT!

WHO'S GOING TO TAKE THEM, ROY?

MYSELF... VIC GUTHRIE ... BLACKIE... CARL HUNT...

...AND DUNCAN!

WHAAAAT!

LET ME GO FIRST, ROY! I WON'T MESS ABOUT THIS TIME!

1984-85

MELCHESTER ROVERS

EUROPEAN CUP-WINNERS' CUP
TEAM LINE-UP

1
STYLES

2   **5**   **6**   **3**
BAXTER   **GUTHRIE**   **BUTLER**   **MCKAY**

7   **8**   **4**
SLADE   **GRAY**   **HUNT**

10   **9**   **11**
RICHARDS   **RACE**   **JONES**

MELCHESTER ROVERS 2   REAL SANTANA 2
(ROVERS WIN 5-3 ON PENALTIES)

AN OPEN AND SHUT-OUT CASE FOR THE DEFENCE

JULY '85

Melchester Rovers Past v Present

ROVERS PAST - LEFT TO RIGHT:
(TOP) KEN COOPER, TUBBY MORTON, TERRY WEST
(MIDDLE) GEOFF GILES, ANDY CROYDON, PACO DIAZ, TOM DAWSON
(BOTTOM) DEREK MILLAR, MERVYN WALLACE, LOFTY PEAK (CAPT.), TAFFY MORGAN, JUMBO TRUDGEON

Roy soon realised he had more than an exhibition match on his hands. When Rovers' Past took control of the game, it highlighted Rovers' weaknesses. With a hat-trick by Geoff Giles and a goal from Lofty Peak, the more experienced side inflicted a humiliating 4-3 defeat over Roy's team whose three goals came from Blackie Gray, Carl 'The Hunter' Hunt, and Roy himself.

AUGUST '85

Rovers started the Canon league season with an equally disappointing performance.

Melchester Rovers 1   Carford City 2
Race

Clearly concerned about his team's lacklustre start to the season, Roy embarked on a spending spree to inject much needed new talent into his squad. Into the side in place of the unhappy Mark Butler came former Liverpool and England player, Emlyn Hughes and ex-Arsenal and Scotland goalkeeper Bob Wilson who took over from injured Andy Styles.

Hughes and Wilson made their debut for Rovers at home to Tynecaster United. Hughes scored on his debut.

Melchester Rovers 2   Tynecaster United 1
Hughes, Race

SEPTEMBER '85

Roy balanced experience with raw enthusiasm, signing up two young London boys, Martin Kemp and Steve Norman, who were members of chart-topping pop group, Spandau Ballet. But Roy was reluctant to include the novices in first team games.

OCTOBER '85

Portdean 1   Melchester Rovers 3
Hunt, Jones, Race

Blackport Rovers 1   Melchester Rovers 1
Race

A disappointing draw for Rovers and Roy decided to name Martin Kemp as substitute for Rovers' next game.

NOVEMBER '85

Kemp replaced an injured Blackie Gray and immediately hit top form.

Melchester Rovers 6   Stambridge 1
Gray, Race (2),
Kemp, Hunt, Logan

MARTIN KEMP SCORES HIS FIRST GOAL FOR ROVERS

NOVEMBER '85

Deans Park 0   Melchester Rovers 1
Richards

DECEMBER '85

Steve Norman was selected as substitute against Carford City in the Milk Cup. In the second half, Norman made his debut, coming on for an injured Emlyn Hughes.

Milk Cup 4th Round
Melchester Rovers 5   Carford City 0
Richards,Hunt,
Race (2), Guthrie

Rovers maintained good form in the league.

Melchester Rovers 3   Tynecaster United 0
Race (3)

After this triumph, goalkeeper Bob Wilson set Rovers a target of surpassing the league record of eleven straight games without conceding a goal.

Melchester Rovers 1   Kelburn 0
Race

JANUARY '86

Milk Cup 5th Round

Walford Rovers 0   Melchester Rovers 1
Race

No goals, but a clean-sheet in the league.

Melchester Rovers 0   Weston Villa 0

Goalkeeper Walter Williams joins Kingsbay.

MARCH '86

Milk Cup Semi-final
1st Leg
Gatesfield (Div.2) 0   Melchester Rovers 2
Race, Kemp

2nd Leg
Melchester Rovers 1   Gatesfield 0
Race
(Rovers win 3-0 on agg.)

APRIL '86

ROVERS' GRAND FINALE

Through to their first Milk Cup Final, Rovers have double cause for celebration with news that Bobby Robson has selected Roy for England's 1986 World Cup squad. Riding on a wave of euphoria, Roy has remained level-headed, leading his team to a hat-trick of league wins against Redstoke, Oldfield and Rotherton.
With newcomers Kemp and Norman backed by Wilson and Hughes, Rovers have been scoring goals whilst remaining water-tight at the back.
Rovers' impressive 2-0 win at Rotherton with goals from Race and McKay saw them equalling the league record of eleven consecutive clean-sheets. Roy Race will be looking to round-off this memorable season with a grand finale win. If Bob Wilson can lock Tynecaster out, then yet another record will fall to mighty Melchester.

BOB WILSON – CLEAN SHEET KING

AND HERE COME THE TEAMS FOR THE SECOND-HALF OF THIS MILK CUP FINAL BETWEEN *MELCHESTER ROVERS* AND *TYNECASTER UNITED!* THERE'S STILL NO SCORE. ANY LAST COMMENTS ON THE GAME SO FAR, BOBBY?

APART FROM *ROY RACE*, AND ONE OR TWO OTHERS, IT'S BEEN A VERY DISAPPOINTING PERFORMANCE FROM MOST OF THE ROVERS...

...RACEY'S HAD ABSOLUTELY *NO* SUPPORT! WHATEVER HE SAID TO HIS PLAYERS AT HALF-TIME, THAT MELCHESTER DRESSING-ROOM MUST HAVE BEEN A DRAMATIC PLACE TO BE IN!

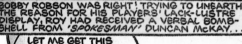

BOBBY ROBSON WAS RIGHT! TRYING TO UNEARTH THE REASON FOR HIS PLAYERS' LACK-LUSTRE DISPLAY, ROY HAD RECEIVED A VERBAL BOMBSHELL FROM *'SPOKESMAN'* DUNCAN McKAY...

LET ME GET THIS STRAIGHT! SOME OF YOU ARE CONVINCED THAT YOU WON'T BE AROUND NEXT SEASON ...BECAUSE *I'VE* DECIDED TO REBUILD THE TEAM.?

AYE! WE'VE SENSED IT FOR SOME TIME, ROY...

...AND WE DON'T SEE WHY WE SHOULD FLOG OURSELVES INTO THE GROUND FOR A CLUB THAT'S ABOUT TO DUMP US ON THE SCRAP-HEAP!

...IF YOU DON'T WANT TO PLAY FOR *ME*, OR THE *CLUB*, OR ALL THOSE *FANS* OUT THERE, NOT TO MENTION *MILLIONS* OF TELEVISION VIEWERS...

I SEE. WELL, EVEN IF I *HAD* ANY PLANS TO THROW OUT HALF THE TEAM... WHICH I HAVEN'T ...IT SEEMS TO ME THAT THERE'S A LITTLE MATTER OF *PERSONAL PRIDE* AT STAKE...

...YOU COULD AT LEAST BE MEN ENOUGH TO *PLAY FOR YOURSELVES!*

AND, SO, AS THE TWO TEAMS LINED UP...

IF TYNECASTER BEAT US, WE'LL WIND UP WITH *NOTHING!*

WE'RE SUPPOS[ED] TO BE THE BEST IN EUROPE[!]

THEY HAD JUST 45 MINUTES LEFT

1985-86

RATHER THAN SIT ON THEIR 2-O LEAD AND PROTECT THEIR RECORD 12TH
CONSECUTIVE CLEAN-SHEET, ROVERS MAINTAINED THEIR ATTACKING PLAY.

MELCHESTER ROVERS 3   TYNECASTER UNITED O

THE NEW MILK CUP HOLDERS COULD LOOK BACK ON A SEASON
GRATEFUL FOR THE CONTRIBUTION THAT HUGHES, WILSON,
KEMP AND NORMAN HAD MADE IN THEIR BRIEF ASSOCIATION
WITH THE CLUB, WHICH HAD NOW DRAWN TO A CLOSE.

JUNE '86

During the Milk Cup Final some Rovers'
players feared they might not make the
team next season. This prediction came
cruelly true due to the actions of a bomber.

Before joining the England party in
Mexico, Roy had felt honour-bound to fulfil a
commitment to take Rovers out to Basran in
the Middle East for a friendly match. In 1979
Roy had helped set up a football league in
Basran and had coached their national side.
The country's latest soccer-loving monarch,
King Aziz Hasur, had invited Rovers to tour.
New signings, Wilson, Hughes, Kemp and
Norman had completed their contracts with
Rovers and, fortunately, did not make the
trip.

Shortly after their arrival in Basran, the
Rovers' team was imprisoned by the leaders
of a military coup. Their kidnapping meant
that Roy was to miss the Mexico World
Cup, but his, and England's loss, was nothing compared to the tragedy which engulfed
the team.

For all too many members of the Rovers'
side, the 1986 Milk Cup victory was to be
the finale of their careers and the last moment of joy in their lives.

THEY DIED WITH THEIR FOOTBALL BOOTS ON

JULY '86

RADIO MELCHESTER NEWS FLASH

'Eight members of the Melchester Rovers football team have been killed today, the innocent victims of a bungled act of terrorism in war-torn Basran. It is believed that the team's coach, transporting them to safety after a kidnapping ordeal, was involved in a collision with a car packed with explosives driven by a rebel on his way to commit a bombing.
Held captive by rebel forces for days during a military coup, the players, still in their soccer strip, had been rescued by an SAS unit and were on their way home. The whole soccer world will be mourning the loss of so many young lives. The British Embassy informed their relatives before releasing their names.

The list of casualties reads as follows...'

Andy Styles	Slightly injured
Noel Baxter	Dead
Duncan McKay	Slightly injured
Vic Guthrie	Dead
Steve Naylor	Dead
Carl Hunt	Dead
Blackie Gray	Seriously injured
Neville Jones	Dead
Rob Richards	Concussion
Roy Race	Dislocated Shoulder
Kenny Logan	Dead
Jimmy Slade	Dead
Trevor Cassidy	Dead

Our sympathies go out to their families.

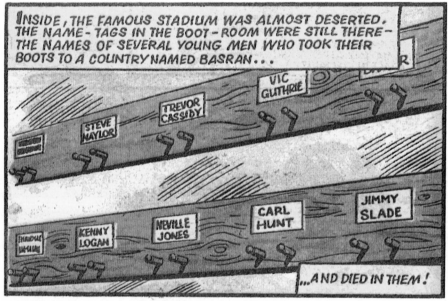

INSIDE, THE FAMOUS STADIUM WAS ALMOST DESERTED. THE NAME-TAGS IN THE BOOT-ROOM WERE STILL THERE — THE NAMES OF SEVERAL YOUNG MEN WHO TOOK THEIR BOOTS TO A COUNTRY NAMED BASRAN...

...AND DIED IN THEM!

Roy slowly began to pick himself up from the terrible tragedy and mourning gave way to a resolve to carry on the Melchester tradition in the name of those who had perished. They had fought with honour for their great club and Roy dedicated himself to continuing their work. His task was a huge one. Only five of the original team survived. But slowly, a patch-work team of replacements grew from the ashes as Roy formed the heart of another truly great Melchester side.

WE'LL JUST HAVE TO BUILD IT UP AGAIN... SOMEHOW!

JULY '86

ROVERS RIDE AGAIN

In scenes reminiscent of 'The Magnificent Seven' Roy is gathering about him a posse of sharp-shooters. The newcomers are:-

Olaf 'Olly' Olsen, a dynamic Danish international midfielder.

Steve 'Nobby' Wooten, at right-back, from Rovers youth team

Mark 'Cracker' Gray, midfielder son of Rovers' legend Blackie Gray

Pak Soon, on the left wing, from Rovers' youth side. Pak came to England as a baby as one of the Vietnamese boat people.

Bruno Johnson, a giant central defender, discovered by Roy playing for Melchester University against Rovers in a pre-season friendly.

Johnny 'Hard Man' Dexter, at left back, arriving on a free transfer from Danefield.

AUGUST '86

Melchester Rovers 5   Deans Park 0
Soon, Dexter, Race,
Olsen, B.Gray

In their first league match the 'new' Rovers were swept to victory on a tidal wave of emotion. "We could have won with a team of apprentices" Roy told the media.

OCTOBER '86

Blackie Gray was appointed assistant player-manager to ease the pressure on Roy.

NOVEMBER '86

To combat hooliganism, Roy launched a membership scheme at Melchester.

JANUARY '87

THANKS A MILLION

Driving home, last night, Roy Race risked his life to avoid knocking down a young Melchester fan. His grateful father, property developer Simon Gardner, has provided Rovers with the funds to build a family enclosure and promised £1 million for donation to the charity of Roy's choice if they win the Littlewoods Cup.

JANUARY '87

Littlewoods Cup 5th Round
Melchester Rovers 2   Gatesfield 0
Race, Dexter

18-year-old Mark Butler was brought on as substitute for injured Bruno Johnson.

FEBRUARY '87

Littlewoods Cup Semi-final 1st Leg
Blackport 0   Melchester Rovers 4
Race (3), Butler

Bobby Robson selected Roy for the England side to play Turkey at Wembley.

Rovers signed 17-year-old right-winger Kevin Clark from Selbridge.

Littlewoods Cup Semi-final 2nd Leg
Melchester Rovers 1   Blackport 3
Race
(Rovers win 5-3 on agg.)

MARCH '87

Rovers signed attacking midfielder Bruce 'Pancho' Miller for £600,000. Miller, who had been playing in Italy, developed a nasty habit of usurping Roy's leadership on the pitch. Roy was to find a novel solution to this problem in the Littlewoods Cup Final against Stambridge City.

1986-87

MAY '87

EUROPEAN CHAMPIONSHIP

ENGLAND V TURKEY
(AT WEMBLEY STADIUM)

Just four days after Rovers' emotional Littlewoods Cup victory, Roy was back at Wembley, this time on international duty playing for Bobby Robson's England side. Roy faced a Turkish team who had built up a reputation for physical play. This became evident as, seconds after the kick-off, Roy was hacked to the ground by two players in a vicious tackle. As Roy received treatment, it looked like he had sustained a serious injury.

170

1986-87

SECONDS LATER THE FINAL WHISTLE BLEW. ROY WAS BADLY INJURED. BUT HE RECOVERED IN TIME TO UNDER-
TAKE, AT THE REQUEST OF THE PRIME MINISTER, A EUROPEAN TOUR OF GOODWILL, PLAYING IN HOLLAND,
GERMANY AND FRANCE DURING THE CLOSE SEASON. ENGLISH CLUBS WERE BANNED FROM COMPETING IN
EUROPEAN COMPETITIONS, WHO BETTER TO HELP ENGLISH FOOTBALL'S BATTERED REPUTATION THAN ROY RACE?

1986-87

IT'S ALL A STORM IN THE FA CUP

AUGUST '87

As part of the club's stand against the growing menace of hooliganism, Rovers' new family enclosure was opened.

In the league, Rovers' start to the league season could hardly have been better.

Melchester Rovers 4   Carford City 0
Soon, Race (3)

OCTOBER '87

By October, Rovers' young side was coasting along in the top half of the table. But one youngster, Roy Race jnr, was making headlines for the wrong reasons.

Roy jnr had run away from home for no apparent reason, leaving no clues as to his whereabouts. Amid worries that the 'King's' son had been kidnapped, the police mounted a massive search of Melchester and surrounding districts backed up by helicopters.

Two days later Roy broadcast an impassioned radio and television appeal for information. But nothing resulted from it. Roy, distraught over his son's disappearance, missed Rovers' next game against the league leaders.

Melchester Rovers 0   Blackport 3

MELCHESTER NEWS
HAVE YOU SEEN THIS BOY?

THE GLOBE
THOUSANDS OF VOLUNTEERS JOIN SEARCH

NOVEMBER '87

Roy returned for Rovers' next game against Portdean in the hope that Roy jnr. might hear the radio commentary. Half-way through the game Roy realised where his son might possibly be hiding. Roy immediately left the pitch and drove back to the Races' old family home and discovered his son living in a tree house.

It transpired that Roy jnr. had run away because he had been dropped from the school soccer team and was afraid that his famous father might be ashamed of him. This was of course far from the truth and Roy explained that he himself did not make his school team until he was thirteen years old – playing at right back if he was lucky!

Meanwhile, without Roy, Rovers lost 3-2 to Portdean, despite a spectacular goal from Bruno Johnson and a charitable Portdean own-goal.

DECEMBER '87

Ben Galloway, Rovers' General Manager, suffered a mild heart attack and Roy was appointed General Manager.

With Roy's family crisis over, he returned to his old form in the league.

Kelburn 0   Melchester Rovers 2
Clark, Race

JANUARY '88

Rovers were fielding so many youngsters, they earned themselves the nickname the 'Melchester Minors'. Teenager Kevin Clark was making his name as a goal-scorer along with Pak Soon. Rookies Terry Spring and Wes Harper were also drafted in from the youth team.

1988 FA Cup Run
Rovers had overcome their usual stumbling block, the Third Round of the FA Cup, with a narrow 1-0 win over Third Division giant killers Carlton City. But they were not out of the fire yet.In the next round hey faced another Third Division side, away from home.

FA Cup 4th Round
Hunsted Town (Div.3) 1   Rovers 2
Race, Miller

FEBRUARY '88

Bruce 'Pancho' Miller transferred to Third Division Dunston Town.

'Pancho' had played a vital role in re-building the team. Although he had been an overbearing and difficult character at times, his experience had been invaluable. But Roy felt it was time to make way for new blood.

MARCH '88

FA CUP 5th Round
Oldfield 0   Melchester Rovers 2
M.Gray, Clark

FA Cup Quarter-final
Melchester Rovers 4   Burndean 0
M. Gray, Clark
Race, B.Gray

Rovers were also maintaining invincible form in the league .

North Vale 0   Melchester Rovers 3
Race (3)

FA Cup Semi-final
Melchester Rovers 2   Burndean 1
Race, Clark,   Johnson (og)

APRIL '88

Victory against Danefield at home would place Rovers just four points behind league leaders Carford City.

Melchester Rovers 2 v Danefield 0
Race (2)

MAY '88

1988 FA CUP FINAL

Melchester Rovers 1 v Weston Villa 2
Race

This was a final Rovers will want to forget. Roy Race opened the scoreline within the first minute of play, but Villa soon swept into a two-one lead with goals from Paulo Cooper and Graham Curdski. In the closing minutes, Rovers won a penalty, but Roy missed it, shattering dreams of a League Cup Double.

Rovers could still win the First Division, if they defeat Stambridge in the final match of the season.

ROY'S GOAL GAVE ROVERS THE LEAD, BUT IT WASN'T ENOUGH TO WIN THE CUP.

1987-88

ALL THIS TAP-AND-RUN STUFF WON'T BRING US THE CHAMPIONSHIP!

IT'S THE TAP-AND-RUN STUFF THAT'S TAKEN THE PRESSURE OFF US!

AYE! YOU TOLD WES, OLLIE AND PAK TO JUST KNOCK IT AROUND... KEEP POSSESSION... DIDN'T YOU, BOSS?

ER, SORT OF...

KEVIN CLARK!

NO...ROY'S DUMMIED IT! WHAT A CHANCE FOR CLARKY!

HE CAN'T MISS...

WITH ONLY A FEW MINUTES LEFT, ROY BROUGHT ON TERRY SPRING — MASTER OF THE LONG, CURVING CROSS...

THIS ONE'S SPOT ON!

FAR POST — AIMED AT ROY!

ONE POINT, ONLY STYLES, THE ROVERS' R, REMAINED IN ELCHESTER HALF...

1987-88

EVERY MONDAY 20th AUGUST, 1988 30p

£I.R. 0.44 (inc. VAT), Australia $1.20, New Zealand $1.35 (inc. G.S.T.), Malaysia $1.60

Roy of the Rovers

MELCHESTER ROVERS F.C.

BACK ROW (FROM LEFT)
STEVE 'NOBBY' WOOTEN, CHARLIE 'THE CAT' CARTER, DUNCAN MCKAY
MIDDLE ROW:
MARK 'CRACKER' GRAY, BRUNO JOHNSON, JOHNNY 'HARDMAN' DEXTER, BLACKIE GRAY, OLAF 'OLLY' OLSEN
FRONT ROW:
MARK BUTLER, ROB RICHARDS, ROY RACE, PAK SOON, KEVIN CLARK

1987-88

CHARITY BEGINS AT HOME BUT ENDS AT WEMBLEY

AUGUST '88

Disaster at Mel Park

Disaster has struck the Mel Park home of Melchester Rovers in the form of a massive earthquake.

Ten minutes into Rovers' opening league game against Blackport, the pitch opened up and the goalposts disappeared into huge chasms. Only some clever footwork saved the players from being swallowed up under the hallowed turf.

Miraculously, there were only a few minor injuries amongst the crowd. Nevertheless, Mel Park has been destroyed and Rovers may never play there again. It is believed that the 'quake' was caused by the collapse of old mining tunnels following the extension of Melchester's underground system.

SEPTEMBER '88

Melchester Rovers v Deans Park

It looked like Cup Final day as Melchester's fans streamed into Wembley Stadium for a taste of history – Rovers' first home game, against London side, Deans Park.

Radio Melchester was there to cover the historic game...

" And a nervous start by Rovers' 'Hard Man' Johnny Dexter, he's let 'Titch' Norris bundle him off the ball, this looks dangerous, but good covering by Race, he's everywhere today! Now, Melchester building again, McKay, to Gray, lovely ball to Johnson...he walked through that tackle, up to Johnny Dexter out left, this looks better, he's taken it wide, Race has lost his marker in the centre, he's calling for it..Race...goallll, Rovers one-nil.

'.....Corner to Rovers, Race in the box, he's flicked it over to Johnny Dexter, wide open, ooh, but wide of the mark, what a sitter he panicked, Roy won't be too happy with that one!'

...LATER
'Free kick to Deans Park, big Tom O'Callaghan, the 'Waterford Wizard' to take it, Picked up by Peter Chapman storming down the wing, what a run. Cross to Edwards, he's broken through Rovers' defence, offside, surely! No the Ref's waving play on, Rovers are stranded, Edwards to Len Jones, back to Edwards, beautiful one-two, only the goalie to beat, he's turned him. Gooalll! Superb strike by Jeremy Edwards.

TEN MINUTES INTO THE SECOND HALF...

'Deans Park are in overdrive now, they're really taking the game to Rovers, ooh saved Andy Styles but it's hit the post, it's anyone's. Goal Deans Park! Les Walters, what an opportunist....two-one, Rovers are in deep trouble now'

....' Beautiful cross from Rob Richards, it's Race in the box, where did he come from? Oh he's down that 's got to be..yes penalty to Rovers. Now who's going to take it? surely the 'Boss', no he's calling over Johnny Dexter, he's not lost faith in the 'the hard man' despite Dexter's nervous start. It's there! and it's all over, a dramatic end to an historic game.'

AUGUST '88

The reigning league champions were homeless, but although badly shaken by the drama, they managed to keep their feet in their next game, away to Portdean.

Portdean 1   Melchester Rovers 3
            Clark, Race, B.Gray

At the interval Roy had received a telephone call with an amazing offer which he immediately accepted. So it was that until the extensive repairs to Mel Park had been completed, Rovers 'home' ground was to be Wembley Stadium!

OCTOBER '88

Tynecaster 1   Melchester Rovers 1
               Soon

But Rovers' occupation of Wembley Stadium was not welcomed by all. Other clubs, particularly London sides, resented what they saw as Rovers' 'promotion' to Wembley Stadium. But history would show that the great stadium gave Rovers no advantage whatsoever. Melchester were performing badly in the league thanks to a poor 'home' record.

NOVEMBER '88

Rovers faced their next league match at 'home' saddled by injuries. Their sad state was reflected in the score.

Melchester Rovers 3   Burndean 6
Race (2), Spring

FEBRUARY '89

FA Cup Fourth Round
In one of the most unsettling seasons in their long history, Rovers were to face yet another disaster.

Hosting a press conference to unveil the newly-refurbished Mel Park, Roy had slipped while playing with Roy jnr. and had broken his right forearm. He was out of Rovers' side against Carlton Town. The question was, as always when 'The King' was indisposed, could Rovers do it without Roy?

Carlton Town 1 [Div 3.]   Rovers 2
Miller   *Harper,*
                           B.Gray (Pen)

As usual, Rovers had faced a tough test against the eager giant-killers. But they came through the bruising encounter with a win and looked forward to returning to Mel Park for the fifth Round against Burndean.

FA CUP RUN 1988

JANUARY '89

Continued poor form at 'home' meant that Rovers were clearly out of the running in the league. To salvage something from the season Roy dedicated himself the challenge of captaining the first side in football history to start and finish the FA Cup at Wembley!

FA Cup 3rd Round
Rovers 2   Selbridge Athletic 1 [Div. 3]
Race,   McKay (og)
Spring,

MELCHESTER ROVERS V BURNDEAN

WITH MEL PARK FULLY RESTORED, ROVERS PLAYED THEIR FIRST MATCH AT THE STADIUM SINCE THE EARTHQUAKE AND HAD SOMETHING OF A SCORE TO SETTLE. IN THIS TOUGH FIFTH ROUND FA CUP TIE ROVERS FACED BURNDEAN, THE SIDE THAT HAD INFLICTED A HUMILIATING 6-3 DEFEAT OVER ROVERS AT WEMBLEY STADIUM IN THE LEAGUE. NOW ROVERS WERE AT LAST BACK ON HOME TURF AND LOOKING FOR GOALS. BUT ROY WAS STILL NURSING A BROKEN ARM AND HAD NAMED HIMSELF AS SUBSTITUTE. EARLY IN THE GAME, ROVERS' KEVIN CLARK WAS HACKED TO THE GROUND IN A VICIOUS TACKLE BY BURNDEAN'S STEVE 'SCOUSER' WILSON. BROKEN ARM OR NOT, ROY NOW HAD TWO GOOD REASONS TO EXACT REVENGE ON BURNDEAN, AND IN THE ONLY WAY HE KNEW HOW...

MARCH '89

The Burndean victory was a gem of a match in an otherwise mediocre season. Rovers had posted much higher margins of victory in their time, but this score was a new record against Burndean and that was all that mattered to them at that moment.

Soon after, the team's jubilation turned to disappointment in the next round of the cup.

FA Cup Quarter-final
Bradfield Town [Div.3] 2   Rovers 1
Clark

MAY '89

As Rovers travelled the short journey across the River Mel to face local rivals Melboro' for their last match of the season, they were staring relegation in the face. Rovers had to win to avoid dropping into the bottom three. Melboro' were eager to be the team to send the great Melchester Rovers down, a factor which gave this traditionally hard fought local derby extra edge.

With the bit firmly between their teeth, Melboro' took an early lead from a free kick. Then Roy burst through to equalise with a left foot rocket.

Rovers came out after the break determined to take the match to Melboro'. Bruno Johnson made it two-one to the Rovers. Then Roy, in unstoppable form, put the win beyond doubt with a classic drive from forty yards out.

Melboro' 1   Melchester Rovers 3
Race (2)
Johnson

TO BUY OR NOT TO BUY THAT IS TEAM SELECTION

JULY '89

Olly Olsen, homesick for his native land, returned to Denmark.

AUGUST '89

Rovers signed 17-year-old Gary Gunn, son of Roy's pal, Portdean Manager, Richie Gunn.

AUGUST '89

Melchester Rovers v Walford

In Rovers opening league game Roy shot immediately into goal-scoring mode...

But Rovers failed to capitalize on their possession and came away with a 2-2 draw.

AUGUST '89

With Olsen gone and Rob Richards out through injury, director Charlie Sutton, pressed for a big-name acquisition. Sutton's number one candidate was Scottish striker, Andy Maclaren, Glenrath Celtic's 'goal-machine'. Roy disagreed with his director..

SEPTEMBER '89

A benefit match for Mel Stone, skipper of Glenrath gave Roy his first sight of Maclaren. It turned into a strikers' head-to-head.

Glenrath 2   Melchester Rovers 2
Maclaren(2) Race (2)

OCTOBER '89

Littlewoods Cup 3rd Round
Melchester Rovers 6   Selbridge United 1
Race (4), Clark
Harper

Under severe pressure to buy Maclaren, Roy had made his point that Rovers' already had a goal-machine on the pitch. He proved that Rovers could score a pile of goals without the need of expensive 'imports'.

NOVEMBER '89

ROVERS BREAK BRITISH TRANSFER RECORD

£3 MILLION MACLAREN

Strangely enough, Roy Race wasn't exactly jubilant at capturing the talented striker, Andy Maclaren who has scored more goals than any other player in British soccer this season. Rumour has it that it was director Charlie Sutton (pictured far right) who engineered the whole deal, despite the misgivings of his player-manager.

1990 FA CUP RUN

JANUARY '90

FA Cup 3rd Round
Rovers avoided a major cup upset...just.

Melchester Rovers 1   Stockley Town 0
Clark

FEBRUARY '90

Littlewoods Cup 5th Round
Danefield 2   Melchester Rovers 1
Race

Roy was forced to bow to the directors' pressure and change Melchester's style of play to suit Maclaren and it hadn't worked. Maclaren was a target man, not a playmaker, so Roy introduced a new 4:4:2 line-up formation to supply him. But the system 'blew up' against Danefield in the Cup.

Charlie Sutton called for the resignation of Roy Race as player-manager for failing to integrate Maclaren.

Roy decided to lie low for a few days while the situation cooled down thus missing Rovers' next cup match.

FEBRUARY '90

FA Cup 5th Round
Rovers 3   Stambridge 0
K.Clark,
Dexter,
Maclaren

The team had proved that Roy was right, Rovers had won in the 'Melchester Way'. Maclaren had been 'converted' and was now thoroughly immersed in their style of possession play. Maclaren was even taking throw-ins! Roy was totally vindicated.

FEBRUARY '90

Charlie Sutton resigned from Melchester.
Thanks to excellent results, Rovers' new twin strike-force of Race and Maclaren was nicknamed 'Double Dynamite'.

NOVEMBER '89

Littlewoods Cup 4th Round
Barndale Athletic v Melchester Rovers

Rovers may have signed up Andy Maclaren, but it was a decision taken over Roy's head and he was not happy. Roy caused a storm of controversy by naming the new £3 million striker as substitute for this vital cup game away to Second Division Barndale.
If Roy was angry, so was Sutton, who had been responsible for purchasing Maclaren; so were the Melchester fans who couldn't wait to see the Scottish goal-machine in action. But angriest of all was Maclaren himself. The hot-tempered, red-headed striker sat seething on the bench aching to get stuck in and end his side-lined humiliation. It looked like he was destined to sit this one out. But when Dexter went off injured, Maclaren came on. With Melchester in attack, Barndale's defence panicked and a miss-cued clearance fell to Maclaren who hammered in his first goal for Rovers, quickly followed by a second to put Rovers into the next round.

APRIL '90

FA Cup Quarter-final
Melchester Rovers 1   Carford City 0
Race

FA Cup Semi-final
Deans Park 1   Melchester Rovers 3
Johnson, Race (2)

Rovers were through to Wembley and a repeat of the 1988 final, which they had lost to Weston Villa

Radio 1 DJ Simon Mayo was offered the position of honorary vice president of Melchester Rovers and he accepted the post.

MAY '90

FA CUP FINAL

MELCHESTER ROVERS v WESTON VILLA
AT WEMBLEY STADIUM

With injury worries behind them Rovers were at full strength for the final, but 17-year-old Gary Gunn – who had made his team debut in the Quarter-final against Carford City and played well in the Semi-final versus Deans Park – was relegated to the substitute's bench. Since helping Rovers through to the final, Gunn had enjoyed the attentions of a media delighted to have found a young star making a fairytale start to his career. His Wembley debut had seemed a formality, but Gunn's bubble had burst and the fiery youngster was at first devastated. But club insiders knew that Roy had enlisted the help of Gary's father to cushion the blow after the player-manager had visitied his latest recruit to break the news...

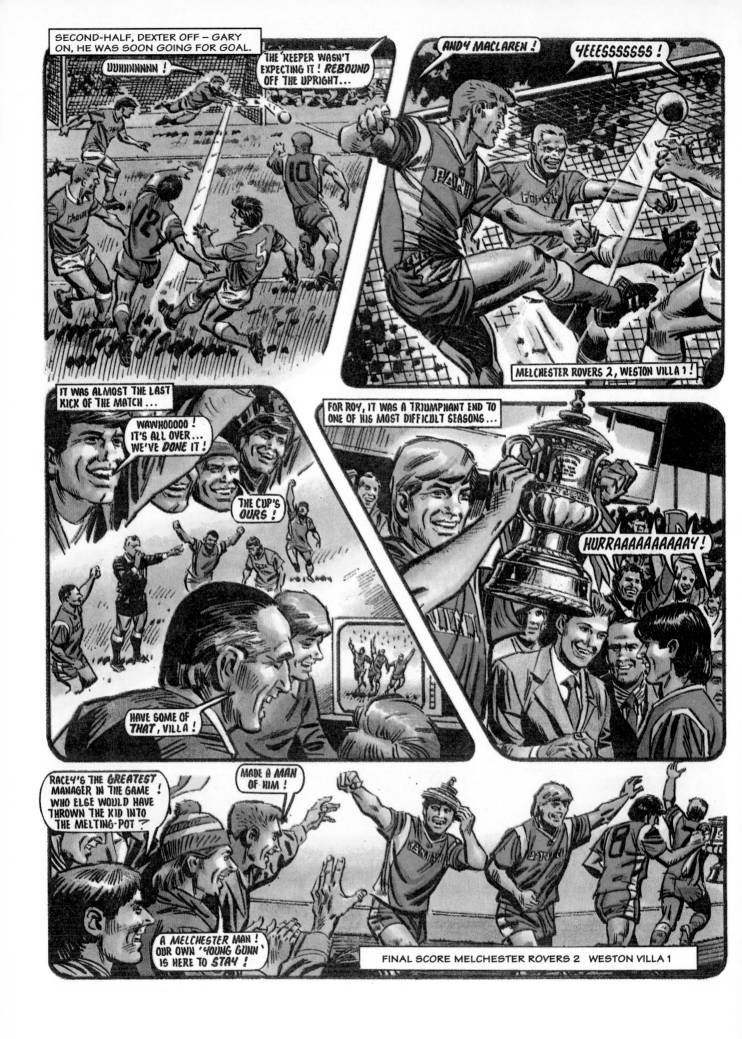

YOUNG GUNS, TOO

AUGUST '90

Bruno Johnson left Rovers and returned to Melchester University to complete his degree in music.

Several new names appeared on Rovers' team sheet – Des Chapman, Broz Bamber and Alex Ritchie – were drafted in from the Melchester youth squad.

AUGUST '90

The youngsters came through their first league of the season with distinction.

Melchester Rovers 4 Gatesfield 0
Gunn (2), Race, Wooten

SEPTEMBER '90

RACE BLASTS SOCCER THUGS

With English clubs re-admitted to European competition, Roy Race today gave a stern warning to all Melchester fans to stay out of trouble and rebuild the reputation of English football.

In his public address after Rovers' opening game of the season against Gatesfield, Roy who is preparing his young side for the European Cup-Winners' Cup, said:

"Matches will be played on a home-and-away basis...which means that many of you will be following us to the countries that we visit.Your behaviour will decide whether we stay in Europe...or are kicked out again...perhaps forever!"

"So if anyone has got any ideas about causing trouble...be warned! I'll find out who you are...and I will get you banned from football grounds for the rest of your life. People who treasure our national game don't want you. I don't want you."

...AND MOST OF ALL, FOOTBALL DOESN'T WANT YOU!

HEAR, HEAR! HE'S DEAD RIGHT!

GOOD FOR YOU, RACEY!

SEPTEMBER '90

European Cup-Winners' Cup
1st Round 1st Leg
Verengen [Belgium] 1 Melchester Rovers 0

The majority of Melchester fans had listened to Roy, there were just two arrests that night. Although Rovers had lost, the battle for peace had been won.

OCTOBER '90

2nd Leg
Broz Bamber and Tommy Johnson both made their first team debut for Rovers and both scored.

Melchester Rovers 3 Verengen 0
Race, Bamber,
T.Johnson

(Rovers win 3-1 on agg.)

OCTOBER '90

Roy's son Roy jnr. was given a trial for the Melchester youth team.

NOVEMBER '90

2nd Round
European Cup-Winners' Cup
1st Leg
Rovers 3 Athletico Zamara 1 [Spain]
Bamber, Race,
Clark

2nd Leg
Atheltico Zamara 1 Rovers 0

(Rovers win 3-2 on agg.)

DECEMBER '90

Duncan McKay was transfer listed.

JANUARY '91

Goalkeeper, Nicky Watson, from Rovers' youth team, made his first team debut in the league.

Walford 0 Melchester Rovers 1
Race

JANUARY '91

FA Cup 3rd Round
Darlboro Town 0 Melchester Rovers 1
Maclaren

Rovers had survived the Third Round against non-league Darlboro in freezing weather conditions. But on the way home, on the snow-covered motorway, a car jumped the central reservation and smashed into the Rovers' team coach. Blackie Gray sustained multiple head and spinal injuries. For a while it was touch-and-go whether Roy's old friend would pull through...

SEE YOU LATER, MATE! DON'T YOU DARE WALK OUT ON ME, YOU HEAR..?

BLACKIE SURVIVED BUT WOULD BE OUT OF THE GAME FOR MANY MONTHS.

FEBRUARY '91

FA Cup 4th Round
Melchester Rovers v Tynecaster

The crash had left Rovers severely depleted of senior players. Roy could have appealed to the F.A. to postpone their next cup game, but he saw it as a chance to blood Rovers' youngsters.

The team was the youngest ever to play a professional cup-tie. Nine players were under 20 years old.

Melchester Rovers 1 Tynecaster 0
Stewart og

Roy dedicated this game to Blackie. It proved that 'Melchester Magic' lived on in Rovers' young guns.

MARCH '91

FA Cup 5th Round
The senior players were fit again but Roy was to regret replacing the youngsters.

Kelburn 2 Rovers 1
Race

MARCH '91

European Cup-Winners' Cup
Quarter-final 1st Leg
Melchester Rovers v Morino [Italy]

Their FA Cup ambitions thwarted, Rovers concentrated on Europe. Morino boasted one of the best strikers in Europe, Zardelli, top scorer in the 1990 World Cup.

Early on Zardelli broke through and took a dive on the edge of the area. It was judged a professional foul and Johnny Dexter was sent off and Zardelli looked very pleased with himself. Andy Styles made a brilliant save and set up a Rovers attack...

1990-91

...REF'S PLAYED THE ADVANTAGE...!

HE'S GOT TO SCORE! THEY CAN'T STOP HIM NOW...!

COP THAT, MORINO!

YEEEEE-YEHHHHHHHHH!

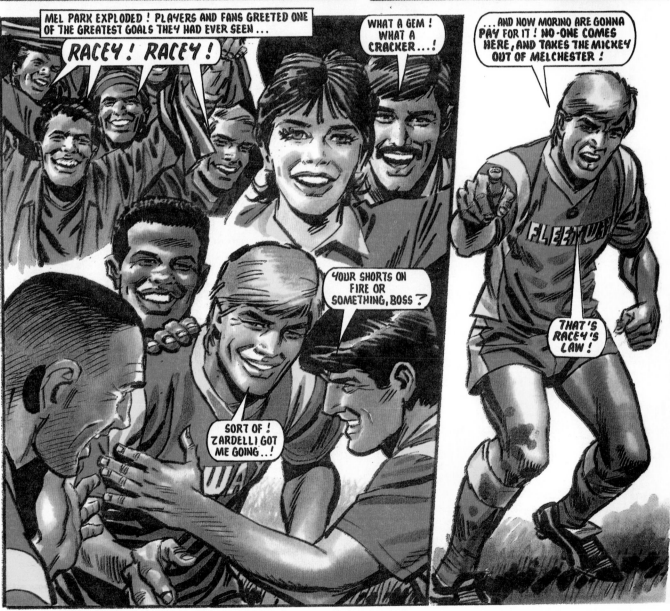

MEL PARK EXPLODED! PLAYERS AND FANS GREETED ONE OF THE GREATEST GOALS THEY HAD EVER SEEN...

RACEY! RACEY!

WHAT A GEM! WHAT A CRACKER...!

...AND NOW MORINO ARE GONNA PAY FOR IT! NO-ONE COMES HERE, AND TAKES THE MICKEY OUT OF MELCHESTER!

YOUR SHORTS ON FIRE OR SOMETHING, BOSS?

SORT OF! ZARDELLI GOT ME GOING...!

THAT'S RACEY'S LAW!

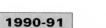

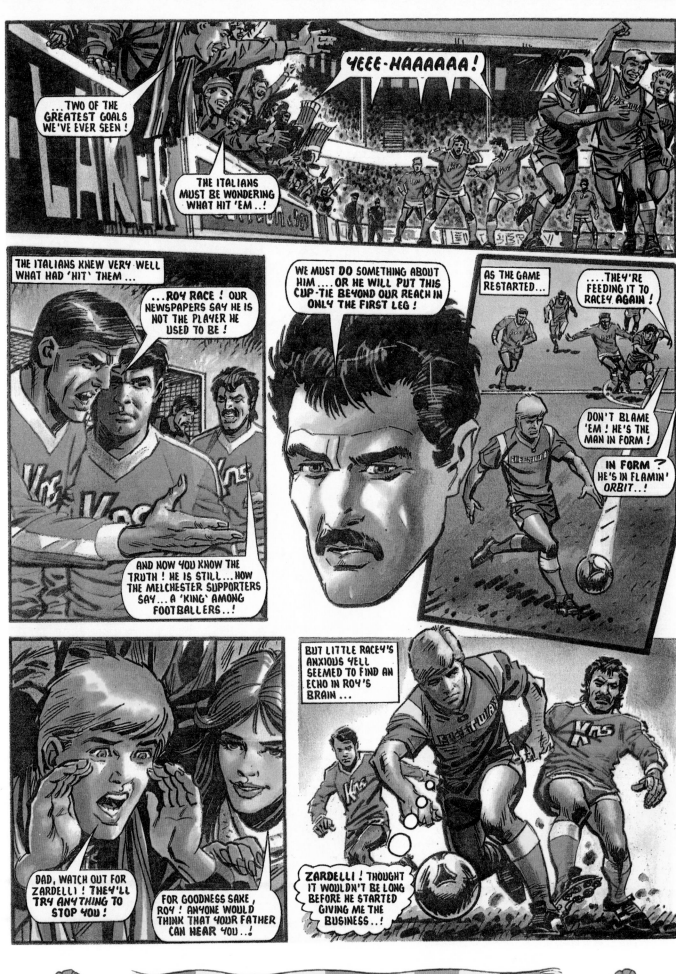

HIGH-FLYING ROVERS GO SUPER-SONIC!

AUGUST '91

RACE 'CHIPS' AWAY AT GOAL RECORD

It looks like 1991 could be the year when yet another record falls to goal master Roy Race – the most goals in football history.

Roy has scored a career total of 421 league and cup goals in his career to date, a fact which has not escaped Dennis 'Chippy' Croker, former Deans Park and England striker and now 'soap-box' TV soccer pundit who holds the record with 435 goals.

Croker, known for his mocking catchphrase "silly ole sport ennit?" has never hidden his jealously of Roy who he sees as the 'pretender' to his crown. He has become Roy's chief critic and on his TV show last night accused Roy of being way past his prime. Croker has set a wager. He will donate £10,000 to the charity of Roy's choice if he beats Croker's record. If Roy fails, he must likewise forfeit £10,000. The bet is on.

...JUST BEEN WATCHING THE TELLY, RACEY ! THE 'CHIPS' ARE DOWN ! HEH, HEH ! BUT YOU GO AND BREAK MY RECORD, OLD SON ! GOOD LUCK TO YER , I SAY !

CHIPPY CROKER

SEPTEMBER '91

Rumbelows Cup 2nd Round
1st Leg
Brenfield (Div.3) 2   Melchester Rovers 1
Race

OCTOBER '91

Rumbelows Cup 2nd Round
2nd Leg
Melchester Rovers 1   Brentfield 1
Race

(Brentfield win 3-2 on agg.)

Rovers' youngsters were finding it hard. Roy agreed with the board that they needed a player with a solid all-round game who would add stability at the back.

OCTOBER '91

UEFA Cup 2nd Round
1st Leg
Roy soon discovered a candidate playing for Bresden, Karl 'Bresden Bull' Bruckner. Karl was a German international and one of the world's most feared attacking defenders.

Melchester Rovers 1   Bresden [Germany] 1
Race

Bruckner played brilliantly, he marshalled his defence with authority and motivation, the very qualities that Roy needed.

NOVEMBER '91

UEFA Cup 2nd Round
2nd Leg
Bresden 0   Melchester Rovers 0

(Bresden win 2-1 on away goals rule)

Rovers travelled to West Germany looking for a win. But Bruckner continued his defensive excellence by locking out repeated attacks on the Bresden goal. Rovers were out.

DECEMBER '91

Rovers signed Karl Bruckner.

Div.1
Melchester Rovers 3   Castlemere 1
Maclaren,
Bruckner,
Race,

JANUARY '92

FA Cup 3rd Round
Aylbury 0 (Div. 4)   Melchester Rovers 1
Race

FEBRUARY '92

FA Cup 4th Round
Melchester Rovers 1   Walford Rovers 0
Race

Roy went off with a gashed leg and Blackie Gray made a welcome return after months

out of the game. Roy still needed eight goals to take Chippy's record.

Of more importance to Roy, Rovers were lying fourth from the top and the League and Cup Double was still on, but Roy's leg injury would keep him out of the vital Fifth Round tie away to Weston Villa.

MARCH '92

FA Cup 5th Round
Weston Villa 0   Melchester Rovers 3
Maclaren, Chapman,
Bruckner

MARCH '92

Rovers signed goalkeeper Nick 'Rapper' Hardisty from Third Division Railford Town for £1 million.

Div. 1
Melchester Rovers 1   Holverton 1
Race

Roy needed seven more goals to break the record.

APRIL '92

FA Cup Quarter-final
Melchester Rovers 6   Gatesfield 0
Race (3),
Maclaren,
Spring (2)

ROY'S FIRST GOAL AGAINST GATESFIELD

With Gunn injured, another goal scorer was needed fast! Roy signed Matthew 'Cannonball' Croker from Deans Park – Chippy's son! Russell Wallace – Merv's son! was selected for his debut, in the FA Cup.

APRIL '92

FA Cup Semi-final
Melchester Rovers 0   Burndean 1

MAY '92

Rovers needed to win their last league game of the season against Kingsbay to take the League Championship and Roy required just one goal to break Chippy Croker's all-time goal scoring record of 435 goals...

ROY'S CAREER OUT ON A LIMB AND A PRAYER

JULY '92

Rovers signed Derek 'Mozzie' Mostin from Second Division Selbridge Town. During the close season Roy had been player-manager of the England 'B' team, taking part in a four-nation international tournament including USA, Italy and Segovia. Mozzie had played a major part in England's victory and, although a clown at times, showed that he had the potential to be world class.

AUGUST '92

Premier League
Melchester Rovers 3   Weston Villa 0
Mostin, Race, Spring

WAWWWHOOOOOO !

J.W. KENSINGT

FROM PRO FOOTBALLER, TO *CLOWN*...ALL IN ONE EASY MOVE !

WHAT A NUTTER! MOZZIE'S GONE TOTALLY OVER THE TOP THIS TIME

Against Weston Villa, Mostin had made history, scoring the first ever goal in the Premier League. But his on-field celebrations upset Chairman Jeremy Sinclair. To the amazement of Rovers' supporters, Sinclair sprang from his seat and stormed after Roy. He ordered Roy to face an immediate inquiry by the board of directors. Humiliated and frustrated by politics, Roy was now thinking that his resignation was the only answer.

AUGUST '92

Deans Park 0   Melchester Rovers 4
Race (2), Mostin,
Maclaren

AUGUST '92

No longer able to keep his place in the team, Johnny Dexter requested to be transfer-listed and Roy accepted.
   Jeremy Sinclair saw this as another opportunity to belittle Roy. Sinclair immediately overruled Roy's decision, further increasing the tension between the player-manager and his chairman.

SEPTEMBER '92

European Cup 1st Round
1st Leg
Rovers 3   Atletico Zarosa [Portugal] 0
Race,
Dexter,
Mostin

SEPTEMBER '92

Rovers were comfortably placed at the top of the Premier League. Their next game was against local rivals Melboro in a match billed as 'The most famous derby in British soccer history'.

Melboro 2   Melchester Rovers 1
Race

The unthinkable had happened, the 'other' Melchester side had beaten Rovers. Aside from his disappointment over this loss, it was obvious that Roy was deeply unhappy with his lot at Rovers. His sullen mood didn't go unnoticed by Melboro boss, Ralph 'Flash' Gordon who had always coveted the job of manager of Melchester Rovers.

OCTOBER '92

European Cup 1st Round
Second Leg

Atletico Zarosa 0   Melchester Rovers 2
Gunn,
Spring

(Rovers win 5-0 on agg.)

OCTOBER '92

The only application for the vacant 'hot seat' was Ralph 'Flash' Gordon. A former England international, Gordon was popular with the players and fans, but under his managership Melboro had not won a major trophy for ten years. Roy felt Ralph would not be right for Melchester Rovers and was determined to ensure Mervyn Wallace held onto the helm. That meant winning games.

OCTOBER '92

ROY RACE QUITS ...ON TV!

Roy Race last night shocked his fans and a live TV audience by announcing his resignation as manager of Melchester Rovers. Hot from leading his team to victory over North Vale with a typical net-breaking 'Rocket', Roy made a live appearance on Sky Sports, with hosts Richard Keys and Andy Gray. But before the interview had started Roy, who had asked to be patched into the stadium public address system, made his announcement to a shocked world:
"This is for the fans. Ladies and gentlemen, boys and girls! at this precise moment, the Rovers' Chairman, Jeremy Sinclair, should be reading a letter that I instructed my secretary to hand to him at the end of the game....It's my letter of resignation. "I will play on – if the new manager wants me to. I just don't look forward to managing anymore. And that's not fair to anyone: Not to my family or the club...or to you, the fans, who have given me such tremendous support over the years...Or to the finest bunch of professionals a manager could ever wish to work with. I'll be glad to continue serving the Rovers as a player, of course. When you see me again – wearing a Melchester Shirt – I'll be just a player!...and, hopefully...enjoying it! "
It is believed that his directors tried in vain to persuade Roy to withdraw his resignation, offering him an improved contract. He remains adamant and has escaped to his favourite haunt, the Welsh mountains.

ROY, YOU'RE WHAT ?

I'M RESIGNING AS MANAGER OF MELCHESTER ROVERS !

OCTOBER '92

Mervyn Wallace was appointed caretaker-manager

OCTOBER '92

Castlemere 0   Melchester Rovers 1
Race

Roy returned as a player but not as manager.

NOVEMBER '92

European Cup 2nd Round
1st Leg
Melchester Rovers 2   Bokeren [Belgium] 0
Race (2)

2nd Leg
Bokeren 1   Melchester Rovers 1
Race

(Rovers win 3-1 on agg.)

Premier League
Rovers 1   Deans Park 0
Race

Roy had scored seven goals in the short time since his resignation.

For the first time in months Roy, relieved of the pressures of manager, was playing with freedom and enthusiasm.
At home he spent most of his time in his office, surrounded by Melchester memorabilia; old programmes, team shots, videos. At first he felt a huge sense of guilt for deserting his post, but that eventually lifted and he enjoyed the extra time he could spend with his family. Rocky, though, admitted that he preferred the workaholic Roy of old.

DECEMBER '92

Rovers had qualified for the group stage of the European Cup, alongside Rapid Alkmar [Holland], AC Gironde [France] and Valmo [Sweden].

European Cup Group 1
Melchester Rovers 0   Valmo 0

Roy had lost his goal-scoring touch, but Mervyn couldn't bring himself to take the 'King' off.

DECEMBER '92

European Cup Group 1
Rapid Alkmar 0   Melchester Rovers 2
Race (2)

DECEMBER '92

The board received a last minute application from Rudi Marki of Lensberg Spartak [Bulgaria], for the manager's job. But it was too late, they had made their decision.

Ralph 'Flash' Gordon had won the day and was appointed the new manager of Melchester Rovers, the papers immediately christened him 'Ralph of the Rovers'.

JANUARY '93

Ralph Gordon announced his playing policy. He agreed that the club's success had been founded on open, attacking football and proposed to continue playing that way. He also wanted to see the full-backs pushing up, overlapping on both flanks. So far Roy had no qualms.

But Gordon was highly suspicious of Roy, and demanded his full co-operation at all times. Roy told him, "My personal feelings don't count, all that matters is what's best for Melchester Rovers."

ROVERS FLATTER TO DECEIVE

FA Cup 3rd Round
Melchester Rovers 3   Burndean 0
Clark, Race,
Chapman

Mel Park hasn't seen anything quite like this barnstorming display by Rovers before – judging by their hair-raising defensive mistakes – it may never again! It was truly a game of two halves. After a quiet opening 45 minutes, new manager Gordon introduced his new system of 'Total football' to Rovers. In the second half every Rovers player was transformed into an attacker. Rovers bombarded Burndean, swarming forward into every gap, from all angles. It looked like total chaos as Rovers marauded like a team possessed. Amid the mayhem they broke through a stunned Burndean defence with goals from Kevin Clark, Roy Race and Des Chapman. But Rovers were caught completely cold to let Burndean through twice with goals from Gowans and McGill. The 3-2 score looked good on paper, but it highlighted the flaws of the new system – Rovers look highly vulnerable at the back.

FEBRUARY '93

Premier League
Tynecaster United 0   Melchester Rovers 3
Race (2), Mostin

Rovers had attacked in wave after wave like a demonic cavalry charge, it was chaotic, but it worked.

FEBRUARY '93

FA Cup 4th Round
Kelburn 3   Melchester Rovers 2
Maclaren, Clark

After leading 2-0, Rovers had thrown it all away and were out of the Cup. Roy was injured and did not play. But he watched from the sidelines and witnessed the short-

comings of the new manager. The new system had proven too rigid and when Kelburn had equalised, Gordon had no answers.

FEBRUARY '93

European Cup Group 1
Rovers 1   AC Gironde [France] 0
Mostin

With Roy still sidelined, Gordon wanted to prove he could win his way, on his own. His hidden agenda was to keep Roy out of the side, the injury was the perfect excuse. But the Frenchmen of AC Gironde came to defend, and defend resolutely. They hardly ventured into Rovers' half throughout the entire game. With ten munutes to go, Ralph relented and brought Roy on. From a corner, 'The King' blasted in a shot which deflected to Mostin who scored. It was Roy all over, it was simple, it was direct and it worked.

MARCH '93

Premier League
Melchester Rovers v Redstoke

True to his nature, Roy had refused to condemn Gordon for his misguided tactical approach. Ever the professional, he stood by his manager's decisions, even though he privately disagreed with them. In an unprecedented expression of solidarity with Roy, the players of Melchester took the initiative and led a revolt against Gordon's new system. The extraordinary events which unfolded at Mel Park were heard live on Radio Melchester...

'Whatever you say about Rovers' new style under Manager Ralph Gordon, you've got to admit it's entertaining. And so is Gordon. Sitting in the dug-out below us, he's always got a smile and a joke for the crowd, despite mounting criticism over his methods.

But what's this?...yes I can confirm, Rovers are lining up in a four-three-three formation! The same as they used before Roy resigned! Sensational stuff, maybe Gordon's had a change of mind.

From the kick off..it's Rovers, controlled build up...Mostin to Race! He's released Matt Croker, what a pass, one side of the park to the other...! And now it's Roy pouncing on a loose pass, it's a solo run, brilliant footwork keeps control of the ball through the tackle, he's dodged full-back Colwyn, he's through, goal!! Roy's just too good for Redstoke! "

..."It's all Rovers now, it might not be total football, but it's certainly total control. They've won a corner, Mostin to take..Racey's calling for it...inswinger...no, it's the old dummy run...Chapman..it's there, two-nil brilliant just brilliant. The Rovers bench are on their feet, but...oh! Gordon's shaking his fists at his team...they're clearly doing everything he's told them not to do. Does he not like that!"

The born-again Rovers continued to bombard Redstoke's goal...

1992-93

ALTHOUGH HE HAD SURVIVED THE HELICOPTER CRASH, ROY'S FAMOUS LEFT FOOT HAD NOT AND IT WAS AMPU-TATED. ROY RECOVERED TO BECOME MANAGER OF ITALIAN SIDE AC MONZA AND HIS SON 'ROCKY' BECAME AN EXCITING STRIKER FOR ROVERS. BUT WHATEVER GLORIES LAY IN STORE FOR THEM, THE WORLD OF FOOTBALL WOULD NEVER AGAIN WITNESS THE SKILLS OF ITS FINEST EXPONENT...THE ONE AND ONLY 'ROY OF THE ROVERS'.

1992-93

HIGHLIGHTS OF THE PLAYING YEARS

(Note – page numbers are in *italic*)

1954-55
Roy Race and his school pal, Blackie Gray, make their debuts for Melchester reserves. *11*

1955-56
Roy and Blackie make their first team debuts, in 3-3 draw, against Elbury Wanderers (Roy scores twice). *13*

Rovers sign striker Arty Hedlow from Elbury Wanderers for a club record £10,000. *15*

1956-57
Rovers sign Frenchman, Pierre Dupont, a winger from Rochemont. *18*

1957-58
Rovers' veteran skipper Andy McDonald's last season for the club. *22*

LEAGUE CHAMPIONS *23/24*

1958-59
Roy is appointed captain of Melchester Rovers, replacing the injured Hughie Griffiths. *25*

Rovers sign goalkeeper Tubby Morton from Tranbridge United. Tubby makes his debut against Bamford Athletic along with new right-winger Dick Stokes. *25*

FA CUP WINNERS 3-2 against Langton United (Roy 2). *26/29*

1959-60
LEAGUE CHAMPIONS *33*

1960-61
FA CUP WINNERS 2-1 against Corstone City (Roy 2). *36/38*

1961-62
Italian club Stadia Batori offer £85,000 for Roy. *39*

Rovers sign Welshman Ossie Jones from the Rhondda Valley to replace centre-half Paddy Ryan. *40*

Rovers play first competitive game in Europe against Schonved of Hungary and lose 2-1. *40*

1962-63
Hughie Griffiths retires. *41*

Rovers sign ex-Royal Marine commando Albert 'Bomber' Reeves at right-half. *41*

Roy makes his England debut against South American side Caragua. England win 3-1 (Roy 2). *43*

LEAGUE CHAMPIONS *43*

1963-64
EUROPEAN CUP WINNERS 3-2 against Nettruno of Italy (Roy 1). *44/46*

1964-65
WORLD CLUB CUP WINNERS 2-1 against Bagota of South.America (Roy 2). *47/48*

Rovers sign millionaire inside-left Lord D'Arcy Plantagenet Trudgeon-Marclay (aka 'Jumbo' Trudgeon). *48*

1965-66
Rovers knocked out of European Cup by part-timers Trondheim from Norway and out of League Cup by Fourth Division side Midbury Town. *51*

FA CUP WINNERS 2-1 against Eastoke United (Roy 1). *53/56*

1966-67
EUROPEAN CUP-WINNERS' CUP WINNERS 2-1 against Alcero of Portugal (Roy 2). *58/60*

Rovers win last League game of the season, 7-0 against Melboro, to avoid relegation. *61*

1967-68
Roy scores his 300th goal for Rovers and breaks a 30-year-old club scoring record. *64*

LEAGUE CHAMPIONS *66*

1968-69
Rovers set transfer record £150,000 for centre-half Douglas Ballard from Carford United. *67*

Rovers sign Lofty Peak from Kingsbay and young midfielder Geoff Giles. *67*

EUROPEAN CUP WINNERS 3-1 against Santova Rapid of Portugal Roy (1). *67/71*

1969-70
Rovers sign winger Vernon Eliot from Eaststoke United. *72*

WORLD CLUB CUP WINNERS 2-1 against Sao Madro Nacional of South America (Roy 2). *72/73*

Roy, Tubby Morton and Geoff Giles selected for England in the 1970 World Cup, Mexico. *73*

FA CUP WINNERS 4-1 against Seaford Athletic (Roy 1). *74/75*

1970-71
EUROPEAN CUP-WINNERS' CUP WINNERS 2-1 against Standard Wasserdam of Belgium (Roy 1). *76/78*

1971-72
LEAGUE CHAMPIONS *80/81*

FA CUP WINNERS 3-2 against Cranville United. *82/85*

1972-73
Rovers sign right-winger Mervyn Wallace from Cranville United, for a club record fee. *86*

EUROPEAN CUP WINNERS 2-0 against Corados of Portugal (Roy 1). *86/91*

Roy and Blackie play for England in 2-1 win against Italy (Roy 1). *91.*

1973-74
Ben Galloway promoted to general manager, replaced as team manager by Tony Storme. Goalkeeper Charlie 'The Cat' Carter makes his debut. *92*

LEAGUE CUP WINNERS 1-0 against Highwood (Roy 1). *93*

FA CUP WINNERS 2-0 against Burndean (Roy 2). *93/96*

1974-75
In the biggest upset in FA Cup history, Rovers lose 2-1 to non-league minnows, Sleaford Town. Team manager Tony Storme resigns. Roy appointed player-manager. *97*

EUROPEAN CUP-WINNERS' CUP WINNERS 2-0 against Niarkos of Greece (Roy 2). *98/101*

1975-76
Roy scores hat-trick for England in 3-0 win against France in the European Nations Cup. *102*

Rovers sign defender Duncan McKay from Portdean for £300,000. *103*

Roy marries Ben Galloway's secretary Penny. *104*

1976-77
Rovers equal league record of 29 games unbeaten. *108*

Mervyn Wallace pips Roy in £30,000 50-goal bonanza. *109*

LEAGUE CHAMPIONS *109/111*

Roy becomes father of twins Roy jnr. and Melinda. *111*

1977-78
Roy takes over as caretaker-manager of England and after defeating Holland 5-1 turns down the full-time job *112-117*

Rovers beaten 3-2 by Alkhoven of Holland in the European Cup Final (Roy 1). *117*

1978-79
Roy offered £1 million to become National Coach of Basran in the Middle East. *118*

Rovers sign Spanish right-winger Paco Diaz from Zaragosa for £700,000. *118*

Roy equals record for the fastest ever goal, scoring in just four seconds against Kelburn in the FA Cup. *118*

UEFA CUP WINNERS 3-1 on agg. against Rassburg of West Germany (Roy 2). *118/124*

Lofty Peak retires and becomes national coach of Basran. in the Middle East.*124*

1979-80
Rovers sign utility player 'Superbrat' Vic Guthrie for £20,000 from Westbury Town. *125*

LEAGUE CHAMPIONS *128/129*

1980-81
Geoff Giles transferred to Melboro. *130*

Rovers sign Nat 'Grandad' Gosden on free transfer from Carford City. *130*

Rovers relegated to Division Two. *132/135*

1981-82
Roy shot! Sir Alf Ramsey takes over as caretaker-manager. *136*

Rovers set a new league goal-scoring record 14-0 against Keysborough. *136/142*

Rovers set new league record 34 games undefeated. *142*

SECOND DIVISION CHAMPIONS *142*

1982-83
Roy's daughter Diana is born. *143*

Mel Park becomes Britain's first all-seater stadium. *143*

Roy resigns and joins Walford Rovers as player-manager. *143*

1983-84
Blackie Gray is appointed player-manager of Melchester Rovers. *149*

Roy is reinstated as player-manager at Melchester *149*

FA CUP WINNERS 2-1 against Walford Rovers (Roy 1). *150/154*

Rovers sign midfielder Carl 'The Hunter' Hunt from Carford City.*154*

1984-85
Test cricketer Geoffrey Boycott is appointed chairman of Melchester Rovers. *155*

Andy 'Streaky' Styles becomes first-team goalkeeper. *155*

Roy captains England against France in 1-1 draw (Roy 1). *155*

EUROPEAN CUP-WINNERS' CUP WINNERS
2-2 against Real Santana of Spain (Roy) Rovers win 5-3 on penalties (Roy 1). *157/161*

1985-86
Rovers sign Emlyn Hughes and Bob Wilson. *162*

Rovers sign Spandau Ballet's Martin Kemp and Steve Norman. *162*

Bobby Robson names Roy in his England squad for the 1986 World Cup in Mexico. *162*

Rovers set new league record of 12 consecutive games without conceding a goal. *163/165*

MILK CUP WINNERS 3-0 against Tynecaster Roy (1). *163/65*

1986-87
Eight team members are killed by a terrorist bomb in Basran. They are:– Noel Baxter, Vic Guthrie, Steve Naylor, Carl Hunt, Neville Jones, Kenny Logan, Jimmy Slade and Trevor Cassidy. *166*

Rovers sign Danish international midfielder Olaf 'Olly' Olsen, Bruno Johnson, from Melchester University, right-winger 17-year-old Kevin Clark from Selbridge.and Johnny 'Hard Man' Dexter, at left back from Danefield. Drafted in from the youth team :– Steve 'Nobby' Wooten, Mark 'Cracker' Gray, midfielder son of Blackie Gray, left-winger Pak Soon. *166*

Rovers sign attacking midfielder Bruce 'Pancho' Miller from the Italian leagues for £600,000. *166*

LITTLEWOODS CUP WINNERS 2-1 against Stambridge City (Roy 2). *167*

Roy scores both goals in England's 2-0 victory over Turkey in the European Championships. *170/172*

1987-88
As part of the club's drive against hooliganism, Rovers' new family enclosure is opened. *173*

Terry Spring and Wes Harper drafted in from Melchester's youth training programme. *173*

Roy takes over as general manager after Ben Galloway suffers a mild heart-attack. *173*

LEAGUE CHAMPIONS *174/178*

1988-89
Mel Park suffers an earthquake and subsides. Rovers play their 'home' games at Wembley Stadium. *180*

Rovers beat Melboro 3-1 in the last game of the season to avoid relegation (Roy 2). *186*

1989-90
Rovers sign striker Andy Maclaren from Glenrath Celtic for £3 million, setting a British record. *187*

Radio 1 DJ Simon Mayo is appointed Hon. vice-president of Melchester Rovers. *187*

F.A.. CUP WINNERS 2-1 against Weston Villa (Roy 1). *188/192*

1990-91
Bruno Johnson returns to university, Duncan McKay transfer listed. *193*

Broz Bamber and Tommy Johnson drafted into the first team. *193*

Roy jnr. signs pro forms with Rovers. *193*

Roy rejects offer of $8 million five-year contract to become manager of the 1994 USA World Cup team. *193*

1991-92
Rovers sign German defender Karl Bruckner from Bresden, goalkeeper Nick 'Rapper' Hardisty from Third Division Railford Town for £1 million, striker Matthew 'Cannonball' Croker from Deans Park. Russell Wallace, son of Rovers' former player now coach Mervyn Wallace, moves into the first team. *200*

LEAGUE CHAMPIONS Roy sets new league goal-scoring record, notching up his 436th goal. *201/205*

Roy appointed player-manager of England 'B' team and wins a four-nation tournament v USA, France and Segovia. *206*

1992-93
New signing Derek 'Mozzie' Mostin, from Selbridge Town, scores the first ever goal in the new Premier League. *206*

Roy resigns as manager live on Sky TV. *206*

Mervyn Wallace is appointed caretaker-manager. *207*

Ralph 'Flash' Gordon is appointed manager of Melchester Rovers. *207*

Gordon resigns and Roy is reinstated as player-manager. *209*

Roy crashes his helicopter and is critically injured and in a coma. Out of the coma, Roy learns that his left foot has been amputated. *212*

1993-94
Roy recovers to become manager of Italian side AC Monza. His son 'Rocky', continues his father's tradition as 'Roy of the Rovers'. *215*